THE
COMB HONEY
BOOK

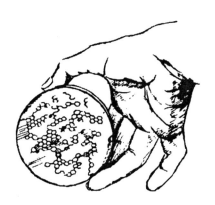

iii

THE
COMB HONEY
BOOK

by
Richard Taylor

Northern Bee Books

The Comb Honey Book
© This English edition Northern Bee Books

Published by
Northern Bee Books
Scout Bottom Farm
Mytholmroyd
Hebden Bridge
HX7 5JS (UK)

ISBN 978-1-908904-18-8

Printed by Lightning Source, UK

For Connie Bright

CONTENTS

PART IV: PRODUCING COMB HONEY COMMERCIALLY

PREFACE

In 1977 I published a little book called *How to Raise Beautiful Comb Honey*. A few years later I re-wrote, extensively revised and added to this to create what I called *The New Comb Honey Book*, *(1981)*. The present book, with the word "new" dropped from the title, is a revision of that one.

The main purpose of the first book was to bring before bee-keepers the specialized techniques based upon what is quaintly called "shook swarming." It was therefore very far from being a comprehensive guide to raising comb honey, and in fact offered little to beekeepers who might want to produce comb honey on a commercial scale.

Since writing that first book I have myself, however, turned my own beekeeping entirely to raising comb honey commercially. In doing so I have learned a lot that seems to me valuable and in these pages I offer what I have learned of the art. The most important lesson I have learned is the need for simplicity. I take the view that a beekeeper wants to produce the most honey with the least work. That, at least, is what I try to do, and here I tell you how. This does not mean, as some might interpret it to mean, that I recommend neglectful or casual beekeeping practice, or that comb honey can be produced without much skill, understanding or knowledge. Simplicity is itself sometimes an art. What is important in successful beekeeping, I think, is doing the right things at the right times and not getting side-tracked into complex and time-wasting procedures.

Although the shook swarm method is quite widely used by comb honey beekeepers, and continues to attract attention, I no longer use it, simply because it takes more time than I am inclined to spend working with the bees. It also tends to result in pollen plugs getting into the supers, because of the reduced brood chamber. Anyone who loves beekeeping, however, should try it, because it sometimes produces spectacular results.

Comb honey beekeeping has been revolutionized, since my first book on this subject was published, by the widespread use of circular sections. The most important development in beekeeping since the second book has been the introduction and spread of parasitic mites. I have therefore added sections on these, as well as on chalk brood, in the present edition.

There are a few things described in this addition on which, although I think they should be known about, I no longer consider very important. I have for example, abandoned the use of bait sections in supers. Some beekeepers strongly recommend them, but I have concluded that they make little difference. Creosote, which I once used on the external surfaces of my wooden equipment, is no longer available, but other wood preservatives are.

If I were asked what I consider to be the single most important idea in this book, it would most certainly be the principle enunciated toward the end (38), which I have (with characteristic modesty) named the "Taylor Principle." Few beekeepers employ it, and yet the advantages have proved, to me, to be so numerous and overwhelming, at least for comb honey beekeeping, that I cannot emphasize it too strongly.

AN EXPLANATION OF REFERENCING

It is important to note that the numbers in the text enclosed in parentheses refer to those numbered *sections* where something alluded to is discussed more fully. They do not refer to the pages thus numbered. For example, the number (39) refers to *section* number (39) where swarm control is fully discussed.

PART I:
THE WHYS AND WHEREFORES

Goldenrod

BEEKEEPING AS A WAY OF LIFE

You have a fundamental choice with respect to your own life. This is the choice, not so much with respect to what you will do for a living, but rather, with respect to what, as a person, you aspire to be. Many people, and probably even most, never really make that choice. Instead, they simply fall into a certain lifestyle, most often the one they find exemplified in their parents and others around them, without considering, or even being really aware, of alternatives. And more often than not, following the most thoroughly established value of our commercial and industrial culture, that way of life turns out to be one of accumulation, that is, the quest for possessions.

But, as people have now become increasingly aware, there are alternatives. Not only is the sheer power to produce goods no longer looked upon as the measure of the greatness of a nation, the ownership of goods is no longer considered the measure of the worth of a person, except in the eyes of a diminishing and vulgar class. You can, if you but take a moment to reflect upon it, actually choose between these two basic alternatives, and then abide by your choice; namely, shall you spend your life in the indulgence of greed, having no more significant aspiration than owning things and pursuing pleasures? Or shall you instead try to make your life itself, especially with respect to the inner person, a work of art? When put in those stark terms one can indeed wonder why that choice is so often so casually made, or why, indeed, so many simply allow it to be made for them by others, in favor of the first alternative.

Is it not time that we thought of our lives as things to fashion in the light of ideals, rather than literally *spending* them in the pursuit of purely mundane and ultimately worthless things, such as riches? Who is more to be envied, someone who has succeeded in surrounding himself with beautiful things? Or one who has somehow succeeded in making his own life beautiful? You can quite consciously make yourself sensitive to nature and to living things, and to thoughts and feelings of people, capable of the passions that animate the poet rather than those that drive lovers of gold, someone, in short, who excels by the quality of your own life, to which you have imparted your own reflective values, rather than someone whose worth must always be measured by things totally other than yourself. There have always been people who have made this choice, the decision to reflectively fashion, rather than merely spend, the life that nature has given them. Thoreau was such a person. So was C.C. Miller, the great American beekeeper who gave up a career in medicine in favor of the beekeeper's craft. What is astonishing is that, considering what is at stake, there have always been so relatively few of these people. It may be that the fundamental drive in each of us is for security. But when that drive claims our very lives and souls then we have, in our desperate struggle for freedom from want, become slaves after all. Everyone, certainly, must clothe his nakedness, nourish his body, and lie down in the comfort of safe shelter; but the thing becomes grotesque when, having achieved these elementary satisfactions, one then tries to indulge them ten times over. This is not, by an enlightened standard, a measure of success, but the purest bondage to the world.

That somewhat philosophical disquisition is meant as a preamble to the very modest suggestion I wish now to offer, namely, that the way of life available to a serious beekeeper offers a special kind of fulfillment. It is no path to power or riches, but it does offer, or at least makes possible, rewards that are vastly more precious. A beekeeper's work can be not merely a means of production, but an art that has its place within the total scheme of life, which is itself an art in the sense I have tried to convey. It challenges both body and mind, demanding not only endurance and strength but the cultivation of great skill, and at the same time calls forth from within one the inventor, the artist, the poet, and the worshipper. The beekeeper has constantly before him some of the most exquisite of nature's creations, often the beauty of nature that no gallery or temple can rival, and through his own ingenuity and skill he is able to offer to others the loveliest product of nature.

By these remarks I do not mean to suggest anything so childishly romantic as that a beekeeper' s life can itself be completely fulfilling. Of course it cannot, and anyone who was simply a beekeeper, and no more, would have a very narrow and trivial existence indeed. If, however, you aspire to an orderly, simple and disciplined life whose rewards are intangible but nevertheless immeasurable, rather than those that are measured by bank accounts and possessions, then you can become a beekeeper with complete fidelity to your ideals. With only a few apiaries, on land that you need not own, and with very little else in the way of tools and equipment, you can be a comb honey beekeeper and by that means alone earn a very substantial part of your livelihood. If your demands on the physical world are truly modest, you can earn all your livelihood this way, incorporating your work into the total deliberate scheme that is your life. Or, depending on your circumstances, location and needs, you can treat this as a considerable sideline to other endeavors, whether this be teaching, carpentry, or whatever. Indeed, your larger livelihood, of which comb honey beekeeping is a substantial part, can be beekeeping itself, that is to say, raising and selling honey of all kinds, and perhaps raising queen bees, and making and selling beekeeping equipment. This whole approach to gainful work is highly flexible, easily enlarged or reduced, and at no point need it violate even the most fastidious ideals of the mind and spirit. It is possible in this world to live a life that is modest in its demands on the world and on others, non-exploitive either of people or of nature, a life that eschews bigness and greed and every assault upon the environment, and it is one of the beauties of beekeeping that it can totally blend with such a life. Other things can too, of course, but still, nothing does so better than beekeeping.

THE ART AND LITERATURE OF
COMB HONEY BEEKEEPING

In the past several years we have seen an astonishing resurgence of interest in natural foods, which is part of the generally heightened awareness of our environment and of our dependence on nature. People have been seeking foods that are unprocessed, foods to which nothing has been added and, more important, from which nothing has been taken. The resulting renewed popularity of honey, which is our only unprocessed sweet, has infused a vigor and enthusiasm into apiculture that has been unequalled since the turn of the century, the period often referred to as the "Golden Age" of beekeeping. More and more people are starting to keep bees in their yards, and the meetings of beekeepers' clubs, which a few years ago were attended by the dedicated and faithful few, are now swamped with new members. 'These people, aspiring to no more than two or three or a dozen hives of bees in their back yards, have little need for the vast treatises on commercial honey production that are so readily available. They have no plans for building honey houses and investing huge sums in extractors and processing equipment. They want instead simple, straightforward methods for getting good crops of honey with equipment they can make or pick up at some nearby store. Simplicity and clarity have to be the marks of the instructions that are offered to them, and this is what I have aimed at here.

Raising comb honey is, essentially, going back to the simple and beautiful art of our beekeeping ancestors, for not long ago in human history all honey was of this form. Combs of honey were harvested from the hives, and either used in that form for food, or the honey was pressed from them and the residual wax was turned into candles. And there is no doubt that such honey was totally good and nutritious, though it sometimes, at the hands of our forebears, left much to be desired in the way of appearance. The honey we find today in supermarkets, which has been blended, heated and not merely strained but filtered and clarified under pressure, may look bright and clear, and it is in fact perfectly good as food, but it cannot compare except with respect to appearance, with the honey that comes straight from a bee tree or, which is about the same thing, straight from the beehive as comb honey, and which is left in that natural form.

Although there exists more literature on honey bees than on any other animal except man, there is today rather little in English that is really very useful on raising comb honey. The classic work in this area is C.C. Miller's *Fifty Years Among the Bees*, but this book is now quite outdated. It will always be worth reading, by anyone interested in bees, but not primarily as a practical guide. Dr. Miller's book is essentially an autobiography, rich in wisdom and the warmth of his personality, into which are interspersed his descriptions of his apicultural methods, most of them valuable and suggestive to a reader; but his system as a whole, involving such things as wintering bees in cellars, could not be used today very well.

The other classic work in this area is Carl E . Killion' s *Honey in the Comb*, published in 1951 and now long out of print. It has now, most fortunately, been entirely revised and rewritten by his son, Eugene Killion. Mr. Killion was a master beekeeper and comb honey producer, but his methods and equipment are likely to appear excessively complex and specialized to the comb honey beekeeper today, especially to a beginner. Some of the specialized equipment Mr. Killion used is not obtainable commercially nor easily made up, and some of the management practices he recommended seem to me, at least, to run counter to the fundamentals of apiculture without sufficient justification, such as dismantling colonies and laboriously cutting out queen cells. Persons experienced in apiculture can indeed study this book with great profit, as I have, but it was not intended by its author as a manual for beginners and backlotters. Its revision and updating by his son, himself a beekeeper of great standing, is a most welcome addition to the literature of apiculture.

Other general treatises on apiculture often have a chapter especially devoted to raising comb honey, but they have one common fault: In their attempt to be comprehensive, they survey various ways of doing things without really answering the particular questions that arise in the minds of those who are just learning the art. They describe the equipment needed, most of which can be learned from any supply catalog or someone dealing in bee supplies, but leave out the very details of management that the reader needs to know. Thus, while most such discussions insist upon the need to reduce a hive to a single story before supering it, hardly any say exactly *how* to go about this fairly laborious operation.

Many of the principles of apiculture that I have set forth in my *How-To-Do-It Book of Beekeeping* apply, of course, to comb honey beekeeping, and I have tried not to repeat what was said there any more than necessary. A few things I have had to repeat, in different ways, for the sake of completeness.

I am much indebted to Raymond Churchill, of Watertown, N.Y., for introducing me years ago to the basic shook swarm method of raising comb honey, which so greatly altered my own comb honey beekeeping; to Dr. Roger Morse, of Cornell University, for his constant efforts to encourage and promote comb honey beekeeping; to Tom Ross, of Massillon, Ohio, and to Lawrence Goltz, former editor of *Gleanings in Bee Culture* for letting me say here some of the things I have already said in that journal.

I hope my little book will be useful, and that it will not only add joy to the hours that some of its readers will spend with their bees under the sunlit sky and amid the bloom of the meadows, woodlands and orchards, but that it will in fact add considerably to the quantity of lovely honey that finds its way into their pantries.

A NOTE ON ROUND SECTIONS

The first round section equipment offered to beekeepers, in the mid-nineteen-fifties, was sold under the name "Cobana," but since the death of Dr. W.Z. Zbikowski, its inventor, other manufacturers have undertaken to supply it, most notably Ross Rounds, of Massillon, Ohio. Virtually all of the large suppliers of beekeeping equipment now offer this product. The dimensions as well as the basic design have been standardized, so that most of it, from whatever manufacturer, is interchangeable.

WHY BE A COMB HONEY BEEKEEPER

There are two especially good reasons for being a comb honey beekeeper, both fairly obvious. The first is the intrinsic beauty of comb honey. The second, which seems to me overwhelming, is the immense saving in overhead expense when this type of apiculture is compared with producing extracted honey.

It is doubtful whether any agricultural product compares with comb honey with respect to sheer loveliness. The honeycomb

A comb honey apiary in Spring.

itself, drawn out to exquisite tenuousness, is a geometric miracle which has awed biologists and mathematicians ever since its extraordinary construction was first studied. Of course this is not apparent in a section of comb that is filled with honey and sealed over, but one catches the hint of it the moment the comb is cut. And apart from this, a snow-white honeycomb, and its association in the mind with the delicate flavors and aromas of the many nectars that yield it, is a refined aesthetic joy not easily duplicated. If you are a comb honey beekeeper, sensitive to this, you view your efforts as something a bit more than a craft, as something of an art; and indeed, you should.

The other reason noted, which is the reduction of overhead costs, perhaps lacks the refined character of the first, but it is of great significance, and is surprisingly seldom noted by any writers on this subject. A comb honey beekeeper really needs, in addition to his bees and the usual apiary equipment and tools, only one other thing, and that is a pocket knife. The day you go into producing extracted honey, on the other hand, you must begin to think not only of an extractor, which is a costly machine used only a relatively minute part of the year, but also of uncapping equipment, strainers, settling tanks, wax melters, bottle filling equipment, pails and utensils galore, and endless things. Besides this you must have a place to store supers of combs, subject to damage by moths and rodents and, given the nature of beeswax, very subject to destruction by fire. And still more: You must begin to think in terms of a whole new building, namely, a honey house, suitably constructed, supplied with power, and equipped. Of course most beginning beekeepers try to meet this last problem by converting the kitchen briefly to a honey house, but in addition to the obvious headaches that this entails, you thereby risk the permanent estrangement of your spouse. Caring little enough for traces of honey everywhere, one's love is rarely enhanced by bees in the house, even when these are rather few. Just one is enough to raise the association with stings.

Now if you are a comb honey beekeeper, you not only need no special building for your work, other than the shop or basement which you already have, you really need no extra hardware at all. Your investment more or less stops with your apiary itself. And unlike the case of extracted honey, you can use your kitchen, if need be, for preparing and packing the crop, and your wife, in case she is not herself the beekeeper, can join you there to share in the work. No great cleanup effort and no dismantling of equipment will be necessary when it comes time to put the super on. Your life will be simpler and, in consequence, your hours spent garnering and packaging the honey crop will be filled with rejoicing, and with fewer frustrations.

All this seems obvious enough, and yet time after time I have seen novice beekeepers, as soon as they had built their apiaries up to a half dozen or so hives, begin to look around for an extractor. It is as if one were to establish a small garden by the kitchen door, and then at once begin looking for a tractor to till it with. Unless, then, you have, or plan eventually to have, perhaps fifty or more colonies of bees, you should try to resist looking in bee catalogs at the extractors and other enchanting and tempting tools that are offered, and instead look with renewed fondness at your little pocket knife, so symbolic of the simplicity that is the mark of every truly good life.

There are, of course, advantages to producing strained honey. It keeps better, and can be reliquefied in case it granulates. Less fastidiousness is needed for producing it, for countless mistakes and blunders, even things as serious as having waxworms or brood in the supers, can be overcome by the simple expedient of straining. Comb honey, on the other hand, must be offered to the consumer pretty much as it comes from the hive, which is an advantage for the customer but not for the beekeeper.

One consideration that served as a strong factor in the trend towards the production of extracted honey was certainly of less validity than beekeepers for a long time thought, however; and that is the greater per-colony harvests that the extractor was thought to make possible. The opinion of experts once was that the production of beeswax in a colony required great quantities of nectar which,

A standard beeway comb honey super.

since it was turned into wax, would never be turned into honey. Until quite recently it was thought that bees could store seven pounds of honey for every pound of beeswax that they needed to manufacture for the construction of their combs—a figure which seems never to have been given any scientific basis, and which is in any case quite certainly wrong. The widespread view that if the combs were used over and over, through the use of the honey extractor, then the bees would be saved the trouble of building them and could convert the nectar thus saved into honey, was only minimally correct. A strong colony of bees will make almost as much comb honey as extracted honey on a strong honey flow. The advantage of the extractor, in increasing harvests, is that honey stored from minor flows, or gathered by the bees over many weeks of the summer, can easily be extracted, but comb honey cannot be easily produced under those conditions.

For a long time extracted honey was much easier to market than comb honey. In fact all kinds of honey were hard to market, in competition with sugar, which was cheap and plentiful, but comb honey was especially difficult. This baneful state of affairs has reversed itself however. Sugar has become quite expensive, and quite widely distrusted as a food, not merely by a fringe of food faddists, but by vast numbers of people who are finally beginning to appreciate the nutritional needs of the human body. Along with this shift of interest has gone an increased interest in comb honey. It has become very easy to market.

There are, then, reasons for raising comb honey. All that is needed is the art—and this, too, is a considerably less demanding requirement than writers on the subject have implied. It is not very hard to raise comb honey. It is not easy to become expert at it, but then, in what art does mastery come easily?

10

THE KINDS OF COMB HONEY

Beekeepers, and even writers on beekeeping, tend to think of comb honey simply as comb honey in square wooden sections. Mr. Killion's book deals primarily with this one particular kind, and it is not unique in this way. Comb honey is, obviously, any honey that is sold and normally consumed in the combs in which it was stored by the bees, and there are several different kinds. Even section comb honey need not be square or rectangular, nor need the sections themselves be made of wood. There have been, since the mid-fifties, round plastic sections. Another popular type of comb honey, relatively easy to produce, consists simply of honey combs cut from regular unwired shallow extracting frames. It is usually packaged in small plastic boxes or, sometimes, little plastic freezer bags, and to distinguish it from section honey it is usually called cut comb honey. Or again, the same unwired frame of honey can be sold exactly "as is," in the frame in which the bees built and filled it. There is no special name for this kind of comb honey, but its advantages are very obvious. And finally, pieces of comb honey can be packed in wide-mouth glass jars, and the jars then filled up with strained honey. This is called "chunk honey," and it has always been popular in the South. It is, of course, a hybrid—half comb honey, half extracted.

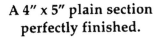

A 4" x 5" plain section perfectly finished.

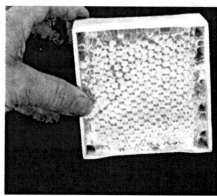

Prize winning beeway
sections

The square wooden sections traditionally used for raising comb honey were the invention of J.S. Harbison, a resourceful California beekeeper of the last century who worked out the idea for sections in 1857. Mr. Harbison was one of the first really big commercial beekeepers, who seems to have enjoyed the notoriety that was inspired by his huge shipments of honey back to New York City. The scope and success of his beekeeping is the more remarkable in view of the fact that he used hives of his own design and construction. The commercial manufacture of wooden section boxes for comb honey production was one of the many achievements of A.I. Root. Today the section box still consists of a strip of basswood, scalloped so that it can be folded into a rectangle, and dovetailed at the ends for snug assembly. These boxes have become quite expensive, which discourages beekeepers from using them, and are also anomalous in that the basswood from which they are made happens to be one of the primary honey plants of this continent.

In the mid nineteen-fifties there appeared, though with very little publicity, a new type of section container that was remarkable in two ways. It was made of plastic, and it was round instead of square. It was little noticed at the time, and for a long time was poorly and inefficiently distributed.

These round sections, then called "Cobana" sections, were the invention of Dr. W.Z. Zbikowski (1896-1977), a retired physician and one-time hobby beekeeper of Dearborn, Michigan. Dr. Zbikowski retained almost complete control of both the manufacture and distribution of this product during his lifetime, with the result that for two decades it was so ineffectively distributed that it remained virtually unknown to beekeepers.

Comb honey can be produced in regular unwired extracting frames, wrapped in transparent protective cover and sold "as is", without cutting any comb from the frame.

The advantages of these round sections over the traditional square wooden ones are so manifest that it is difficult to believe that they will not entirely replace them before long. The round sections have, of course, no corners to be filled, which means that the bees fill them and cap them over in less than half the time required for square sections. The assembly of a round section super is fast—approximately twenty minutes—and the dismantling of the super and packaging of the honey is similarly very fast. The sections require no scraping of propolis, which has always been the most tedious aspect of using square wooden sections. Instead of being wrapped or boxed, the sections simply receive a snug fitting top and bottom cover, resulting in a package that is virtually leak proof, very attractive and easy to stack. The single disadvantage to these round sections is that special frames are needed in the supers, and these are quite costly. They do last indefinitely however—I have some that have been in use forty years with no breakage whatever—and the time and labor they save by obviating the need to scrape the sections makes them well worth the investment. With only a few colonies and a modest investment, a beekeeper can, with minimal time and effort, produce a thousand sections in his backyard each year using this remarkable equipment.

**Dr. Wladyslaw Zbikowski, inventor of the
modern circular comb honey section.**

I consider Wladyslaw Zbikowski the inventor of the round section, even though there were precedents in the history of apiculture. An early writer on bees, who signed himself "The Rambler," had tried to make tiny two-ounce round sections by drilling holes in a small board, lining them with wood shavings, and inserting the board into a hive. And an Englishman, Mr. T. Bonner Chambers, at

Round comb honey
freshly harvested.

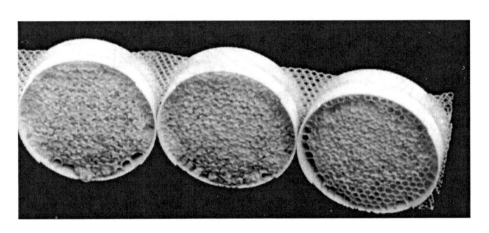

about the same time came up with a somewhat more sophisticated version of the round section. He made a wooden frame with four holes in it, into which he inserted glass rings that he had cut from a jar. The basic idea of this is so strikingly similar to the modern round section that one wonders whether Dr. Zbikowski did not get it from that early source. It is my belief, nevertheless, that the idea was original to Dr. Zbikowski's mind, and that he derived it, not from outdated apicultural literature, but from observing the normal shape of combs as the bees build them in nature.

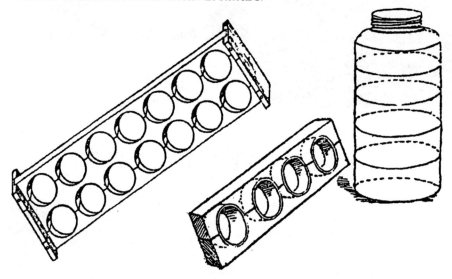

Early forerunners of round sections. Drawing on left, from 1888 GLEANINGS IN BEE CULTURE (p 798) shows "The Rambler's" crude wooden frame. On right is Mr. Chambers' more ingenious wooden frame, into which he inserted glass rings cut from a jar, from the 1889 GLEANINGS (p 42).

Cut comb honey, chunk honey and comb honey produced uncut in shallow extracting frames are of such obvious familiarity that little needs to be said concerning them. To raise these kinds of honey one should use shallow top bar frames instead of Hoffman frames, preferably frames with the top bar split so that foundation can be fitted in easily without the need to fix it in with melted beeswax. Omit wires from the frames, and use only starter strips of thin comb foundation rather than full sheets. Details of these procedures will be given in subsequent pages.

One final kind of comb honey, not included in the foregoing discussion, should perhaps be mentioned, especially since it is gaining in popularity. This is comb honey put by the bees in empty supers, that is, supers without any frames. Just the ten top bars to frames or ten plain strips of wood are used in such supers, with a very narrow strip of starter foundation in each. The advantage of this rather primitive system is that you avoid the expense of frames. The main disadvantage is that the combs must be cut from the ends of the supers, and usually from underneath, and this is somewhat messy. The resulting honey is as good as any, however, and can be used as is or cut up and put in jars with strained honey.

Most methods of getting comb honey work for all the different kinds, which simplifies our task of exposition. The methods of raising cut comb honey, or indeed any honey that is stored in regular extracting frames or in no frames at all, can be simpler and less fastidious than some of the methods of getting section honey. What I shall do, therefore, is describe how to raise section honey. I shall consider first the methods appropriate for small, "backyard" beekeepers, and then describe separately the management of apiaries for commercial comb honey production.

Chunk honey is packed in wide mouth jars and brings a premium price.

Cut comb honey packed in
square plastic containers.

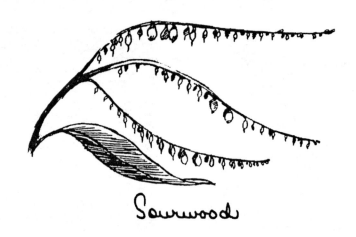

Sourwood

18

THE SWARMING PROBLEM

There is one real drawback to comb honey beekeeping that should not be minimized, and this is, that the problem of swarming is exacerbated. Producing comb honey requires (1) using small hives, either single-story or story-and-a-half and (2) having hives that are very populous. The combination of these obviously intensifies the impulse of the bees to swarm. It should also be emphasized, however, that overcrowding, that is, excessive population of adult bees, is not what causes swarming. Rather it is, more than anything else, the congestion of the brood nest, resulting in a sudden building of queen cells.

The beekeeper who produces strained honey has a considerable advantage here. This beekeeper will normally use two-story hives, and can exchange the combs between the two stories in such a way as to relieve congestion in the brood nest or, otherwise expressed, to keep an "open" brood nest. The comb honey beekeeper does not have this valuable option.

The comb honey beekeeper can, however, do quite a lot to control swarming, and in what follows I shall offer suggestions.

PART II:
BACKYARD COMB HONEY
BEEKEEPING

Black Locust

THE BASIC PRINCIPLES OF COMB HONEY
BEEKEEPING

There is no miracle beehive waiting to be invented; there is no supreme strain of bees waiting to be bred; there is only good management. Our Langstroth wood hive is one of the simplest and most versatile agricultural tools we have. It has undergone no significant change in about a hundred years. It is a virtual certainty that it will never be replaced by something better. Even if a better beehive could be designed, and I believe this is possible, it is doubtful whether it would really be significantly better than what we have, and it is quite certain that it would not warrant junking what we now have. For it must be remembered that one of the chief merits of the standard Langstroth hive is that it is standard, and that hive bodies can therefore be switched from one colony to another, something that is absolutely basic to most management practices. A hive body with which this could not be done would be a poor investment indeed, no matter what might be its other virtues.

As for strains of bees, I do believe that some are certainly better honey gatherers than others, and that some bee breeders do in fact offer superior queens. Still, this is a hard factor to control, given the biology of the queen and the manner in which she gets mated. A backlot beekeeper can requeen every two years and thus keep the stock more or less pure, but a commercial beekeeper can hardly do this. Even the best queens get superseded, through swarming or otherwise, without one's knowing it, and the daughters of those pure bred queens will go out and mate with whatever drones overtake them. Furthermore, even the very best bees will do a poor job of honey making if badly managed, whereas wild swarms picked up here and there, some perhaps issuing from bee trees, will store great crops of comb honey at the hands of someone who manages them with skill.

The management of your bees, then, is the one thing that you really can control, and it is also the one thing that makes the big difference between failure and success.

In the following pages I describe some of the best systems of management of colonies for comb honey, all of which I have used. Some are very simple, one or two are rather complex. Each has its advantages, each its disadvantages, and I shall try to indicate what these are.

There are, moreover, a few general principles of management that always apply, whether one goes in for comb honey or for extracted honey. These are worth spelling out at the beginning, so that they can serve as the background to more specific manipulations.

The four most basic principles are, I believe, these.

1. Work with the bees, rather than against them. One works with the bees, for example, when he padgens them (4), thereby turning to his own advantage the foraging behavior the bees are already engaged in. Using bait sections (16), similarly, is working with the bees, as it simply takes advantage of their propensity to build comb. The clearest examples of working against the bees are cutting out queen cells in the attempt to prevent swarming, or reducing the size of the hive just when the bees are building up most rapidly. Either practice has the effect of frustrating what the bees are attempting to do, thereby squandering, rather than utilizing, their energy.

2. Do not open any colony, or remove any frame of brood, except for a specific purpose that justifies such manipulation.

This can be called the rule of "let alone." A colony of bees does best when interference with it is kept to a minimum. You should not, for example, open a hive just to see whether it has a queen, unless you have reason to suspect it has not; or to see whether it has a good brood pattern unless, again, you suspect queen failure.

Some of the manipulations described in what follows do, indeed, call for rather drastic manipulation of colonies. Even here, however, the work should be done deliberately and quickly, without clumsiness or mishap. Then, when completed, the colony should again be left alone, as much as practicable.

3. Have strong colonies. This means hives that are boiling over with bees. A super half full of bees will not fill with honey very fast. One in which bees seem to occupy every available cubic inch will be filled with honey sometimes in only a matter of days.

If, therefore, you have a weak colony, then do not count on much of a crop from it before fall, or perhaps even the next year, and concentrate your attention in the meantime on the very populous ones, the ones I like to refer to, in my own apiaries, as "busters."

4. If some problems arise, or some colony seems aberrant, and you do not know what to do, then do nothing. Bees have a marvelous capacity for overcoming almost any setback, so leave it to them when you can. Things are seldom made worse by your doing nothing at all; whereas they are often made vastly worse by misguided meddling.

24

In addition to those four general rules to guide your practice, there are five general principles of bee behavior that underlie most principles of management, especially for comb honey. These are:

1. A newly hived swarm draws out foundation quickly and beautifully, including the foundation in comb honey supers if the swarm can be induced to enter such supers when it is first hived.

2. Foraging bees return to the precise location of the hive entrance to which they have become oriented, and will enter a new hive that is there even if their own hive has been moved only a very short distance away, or turned to face in the other direction. If they return to find no hive there at all, then they will, after some confusion, drift to another hive nearby, usually whichever hive is closest to the location of their accustomed entrance.

3. A colony of bees that is deprived of either its foraging bees or of its brood, or even a substantial part of its sealed brood, will not swarm, even though it may have begun queen cells in preparation for swarming.

4. Bees draw the foundation in comb honey supers to the most delicate tenuousness when both days and nights are warm. The cell walls of sections that are drawn during cool weather, on the other hand, are thicker, and the resulting comb honey more waxy. The fairly common belief that bees make honey best when the days are hot but the nights cool is not correct, especially with respect to comb honey.

5. A colony, or part of a colony, that is deprived of its older flying bees—by being moved to a new stand in the same apiary, for example— is easy to requeen, since young bees show little hostility to a new queen or to any other strange bee.

Dutch Clover

1. RAISING COMB HONEY WITH PACKAGE BEES.

There would be no reason for using package bees for raising comb honey unless one were just beginning, and had no other choice. Using package bees for this purpose runs counter to one fairly basic requirement of comb honey getting, and that is, the use of very populous colonies. Besides this, package bees are, of course, expensive.

Still, if you start your beekeeping with package bees, you can, with luck, raise comb honey with them the first year, provided you are in a good beekeeping area. Your crop will be small, but there are compensating advantages. Your bees will probably be of a good strain, and your equipment, assembled by you, will probably be new. Beginning in this way is therefore instructive.

The fundamental thing to bear in mind if beginning with package bees is that the bees you purchase are not the ones that will gather your honey crop. They serve only as a nucleus to get the colony started and growing, and it is the huge population of subsequent generations that will gather the crop. Therefore, do not imagine that you will do significantly better by starting with huge packages. Three-pound ones are adequate. But they will be of little use to you unless you can build them up to maximum strength in the minimum of time.

To do this, arrange to have the bees arrive about the time the dandelions are blooming. This will give the bees an early source of pollen, essential for brood rearing. If the bee company cannot insure their arrival at about the time you need them, then place your order with another bee company that will, and don't hesitate to use the telephone long distance to make sure he's keeping his promise. If it is cold when the bees come, then set them in a somewhat darkened place until the weather warms up into the sixties and is not windy. Meanwhile, feed the bees daily by placing the cage on its side in a basin or tub and sprinkling sugar syrup into it. It does not matter if some of the bees get sticky and drenched, so long as you do not risk drowning them. Then when the day is right—warm and wind free— hive them as follows: Remove a few frames from the hive, already set up where it is going to remain, then remove the tiny queen cage with its precious occupant, sprinkle the bees generously with sugar syrup, and dump them into the space created by removing the frames. Next dunk the queen cage briefly in sugar syrup, so she will not fly off, and liberate her right into the cluster of bees milling about in the hive. Finally, replace the frames gently, to avoid crushing any bees, replace cover, and close the entrance down to a tiny hole, just big enough for a couple of bees to pass through. All this should take only a few minutes. Leave the hive undisturbed overnight. Then the next day, begin feeding the colony sugar syrup. The best way to do this is to poke four small nail holes in the center of the lid of a glass jar—a gallon jar, if you have one – fill it with syrup, and invert it over the inner cover hole. Then cover the feeder jar with an empty hive body and cover, if you have one.

One way to mix the sugar syrup is to pour a five-pound bag of granulated white sugar (nothing else) into a gallon jar and fill it up with hot water. Exact proportions of sugar to water are not very important, provided the syrup is not too dilute.

The secret of getting a strong colony capable of storing a crop of comb honey the first year is stimulative feeding. This means slow but continuous feeding over a considerable period of time, until all the combs are drawn out and the hive is filled with bees. The continuous slow feeding has the same effect on the colony as a honey flow, inducing the queen to prodigious egg laying, and therefore rapid colony buildup. Of course you will see no increase in strength for a few weeks, for those eggs must hatch and the larvae undergo their metamorphosis to adults, and this does not happen overnight. But once brood begins to emerge in the combs, the population growth is astonishing.

Syrup consisting simply of white sugar dissolved in water, as recommended here, is perfectly good for this purpose, and is in fact to be preferred to anything else. The bees build comb as readily from this as from nectar. Of course none of this sugar ends up in the honey you will harvest, because feeding will have ceased before any supers go on.

When your colony is strong and all the combs have been drawn out, discontinue feeding it, put a queen excluder on it and over this a comb honey super. You should not, except in a very unusual and superior beekeeping area, expect to get more than one super of honey from a package colony. Do not disturb the colony from now on except to peer in, from time to time, to see how well the super is getting filled with honey.

When the sections are filled and capped over, with the exception, perhaps, of those in the comer, harvest the super, and give the colony its second story, the one that will be used by the bees for storing the honey which they will winter on. This second story should be a shallow super, if the colony will continue to be used for raising comb honey, but otherwise, at least in the colder climates, it should be a full depth hive body. This hive, either one-and-a-half or two stories high, will henceforth belong to the bees, year in and year out, and supers will be added over it.

By fall this second story should be quite filled with honey. If it is not, then you will need to resume feeding the bees sugar syrup as long as the weather is warm. This should be necessary only in the event of an almost complete failure of the autumn honey flows, which seldom happens.

You will notice that there were *two* special steps in the foregoing procedure which are necessary for getting comb honey from package bees. The first, as noted, was slow stimulative feeding for colony buildup, before any super goes on. And the second was to super over a single story, giving the colony its normal second story only *after* they have supplied you with your crop of comb honey. Comb honey should always be gotten primarily from the early summer flows. Not only are the later flows uncertain, but comb honey that is stored during cool weather tends to be too waxy, and the combs are seldom filled very well. Bees make the best comb honey, and draw the foundation out to extremely refined delicacy and tenuousness, in hot weather, when the nights as well as the days are warm. Of course unfinished sections can be finished up by the bees on the autumn flows, and the honey, though not quite as lovely as the earlier honey, will be perfectly all right.

Some comb honey beekeepers believe you can dispense with the queen excluder, but I think that if you start with a package, and super over a single story, as described here, you should use one. A good rule to follow here is this: Use an excluder under comb honey supers *unless* there is honey stored in the hive below. Honey itself, stored in the combs, acts as a fairly effective barrier to the queen, and since honey is always stored above the brood nest, it usually keeps the queen confined to the brood area below.

2. GETTING COMB HONEY WITH SWARMS.

An insufficiently appreciated value of a good prime swarm is that it can be used almost effortlessly to produce beautiful comb honey. You need only to hive such a swarm on foundation only—no drawn comb—with a queen excluder over the hive and a comb honey super over that. Such a swarm will occupy the entire hive and super at once and immediately begin drawing out the comb honey sections and filling them. But the two essential things to success with this are, first, to use only a large prime swarm, not small after swarms having virgin queens, and second, to be sure there is no drawn comb in the hive when the swarm is introduced into it.

The reason for this is that if there is any drawn comb at all down in the hive, then the swarm simply settles in to build up a good brood nest, entirely ignoring the super, sometimes for weeks, by which time it is too late to take advantage of the energy and honey gathering industry of such a swarm. But if the hive contains foundation throughout, then the super, even if divided from the hive by a queen excluder, is just as attractive to the bees as the hive below, and they distribute themselves throughout, from top to bottom. Thus you achieve at a stroke what is sometimes the main difficulty in raising comb honey, namely, inducing the bees to go up into the supers.

A newly hived swarm is the most industrious colony in the apiary. They are by natural instinct primed to draw comb, and they have no brood to feed. So nearly all the honey goes up into the supers where you want it. If you check the supers the day after the swarm is hived you will find that the bees are already at work there, drawing out the foundation.

Sometimes the bees will soon—within a day—abandon such a hive since, having foundation only, it is not inherently attractive to them. They can be prevented from absconding by snipping off the queen's wing tips, so that she cannot fly. If the bees then attempt to abandon the hive with such a queen, they will soon return, since she will be in the grass in front of the hive vainly attempting to fly off with them. If you then reintroduce her to the hive, the rest of the bees will follow her in, and stay there. By the time the bees have been in the hive two nights they will almost always remain, and in any case the likelihood of their trying to abscond at all is probably less then thirty percent.

Beekeepers unwilling to attempt clipping a queen's wing can, alternatively, simply slip an extra queen excluder between the hive and the bottom board, being sure the queen is above it, and leave it there no more than a couple of days. The queen will not be able to pass through this, even if the rest of the bees do fly out, so they will all return to her and stay there after one vain attempt to leave.

Or again, if you wait until late afternoon to hive the swarm—some time after five, but while it is still daylight—then the bees will almost certainly remain in the hive overnight and, having stayed that long, they are likely to remain for good and gather your crop of comb honey. You could also, of course, ensure their staying put by having some unsealed brood in the hive, but that would be a mistake, for you would get no comb honey for a long time. The reason has already been noted; namely, that the bees would simply settle into the hive where the brood is and ignore the supers.

Of course the larger the swarm, the greater will be your success with this method. A beekeeper can, therefore, simply throw two natural swarms together and use them to make comb honey, in any of the several ways described before.

A good way to do this is to gather your swarms in screened swarm boxes. Such boxes can be made from old hive bodies, and the swarms can be gathered either by shaking them directly into such boxes, or by dislodging the swarm into a huge funnel inserted into such a box, which is my own system. Then the bees can be dumped first from one such swarm box, then from the other, in front of a hive. One of the queens will be lost by this procedure, but the rest of the bees will usually mingle peacefully, since all enter the hive more or less together.

An obvious variation on the foregoing is to make up a two-chambered hive, as described under the double shook swarm procedure (10), and hive one prime swarm in one half and another swarm in the other half. This is exceedingly simple to do. Both queens survive this procedure, so that you get a two-queen colony, and the bees mingle peacefully to build up a huge population, and a very large crop of honey.

This method is, obviously, much simpler than the double shook swarm method described below (10), since it involves no manipulation of combs, and the end result is about the same.

A good prime swarm about to be funneled into a swarm cage, then used for getting comb honey.

Below, the same swarm about to be hived

3. HOW TO USE SWARMS AND SHALLOW SUPERS TO GET COMB HONEY.

If you follow exactly the method just described, but substitute a shallow extracting super fitted with nine frames of foundation instead of a full depth hive body, you will get even better results. But again, you must use a good big swarm, and there must be no drawn comb in the shallow super into which it is hived. Needless to say, you will need to confine the queen to that shallow super with an excluder on top. And instead of adding only one comb super over it, you will probably need at least three. Having put that many on, check in a couple of days, and if bees are hanging out at the hive entrance, suggestive of overcrowding inside, then add still another.

If you use this shallow super method, then you should use only nine frames with foundation instead of ten. Then, after you have gotten your comb honey crop, you can do either of two things. You can, first, unite that shallow super by the newspaper method (14) to the top of another normal hive sitting right next to it, where the thousands of foraging bees will find it, in case there is a normal hive there; or, second, you can place a full depth hive body with frames of foundation of (preferably) drawn combs *over* it, and leave it right there.

If you do the first of these, then the brood in that shallow extracting super will all hatch out and the combs will get filled with honey, the bees meanwhile disposing of the extra queen that results from this uniting. Since there are only nine frames in that super, then the combs can be uncapped fairly easily and extracted, provided you have an extractor. They will, however, be very dark throughout, from having been used by the bees for brood rearing.

If you choose the second alternative, which is probably preferable, then you will of course end up with a new colony. The shallow super can be left permanently as part of that colony if you wish.

4. HOW TO GET A SPECTACULAR RESULT BY SWITCHING HIVE STANDS.

If a large prime swarm, or in this case even a moderate sized one, comes from one of your own hives *and you know which hive that is*, then you can use it to store up a prodigious crop of comb honey by utilizing a simple apicultural trick that has come to be known as "padgening," the word being derived from the name of J.W. Pagden, who first described the basic manipulation over a hundred years ago. All you need to do is move the parent hive, from which the swarm issued, to a new location in the same apiary, and on its original stand set either a full depth hive body with foundation only or, even better, a shallow extracting super with foundation only and, just as described above (3), hive the swarm there. By doing this you augment the swarm by all the foraging bees from the parent colony, since they fly back to the new hive at the old familiar place, greatly strengthening it with just the bees you need for your crop. Add a queen excluder, as before, and then at least four comb honey supers, perhaps more, as needed to accommodate the huge population that results from this. It is not uncommon to get eight or ten supers of honey from this simple manipulation.

The colony that was moved will not throw any more swarms that season, because it has lost all its foraging bees to the new hive on the old stand. It will tear down any queen cells that are there, after a virgin queen hatches from one of them, then this queen will get mated and the colony will build up and store a super or two of honey in its own right.

Now if you used a shallow super for the hive into which the swarm was hived, you are going to end up, after the honey harvest, with a shallow hive which of course cannot be wintered over. The best thing to do with it is unite it with another colony, (14).

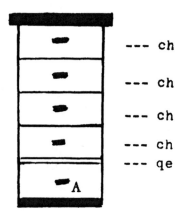

Hiving a swarm in a shallow super and padgening:

1. Move a colony that has thrown a good prime swarm to a new location in the same apiary, and on the stand from which it was moved set a shallow extracting super (A) fitted with nine frames of foundation, on top of which place a queen excluder (qe) and three or four comb honey supers (ch).

2. Hive the prime swarm in that hive (A), where it will be augmented by the foraging bees that remained with the parent hive.

In anticipation of this, a very good and convenient procedure is the following. When you first move the parent colony, and place the shallow super on its original hive stand, simply put the parent colony back-to-back with the new hive. Thus, you will end up with the new shallow hive, having perhaps four or five comb honey supers on it, and, right behind this, the parent hive, facing the other way. Then, when the time comes to harvest the comb honey supers and unite the shallow brood chamber to a normal hive, you need only to turn the parent hive around the way it was in the first place, set it on its original stand, and unite the shallow brood chamber to it by the newspaper method (14). The forager bees from this colony find the reversed entrance after a brief period of confusion, the extra queen eventually gets deposed, the brood in the shallow brood chamber hatches out and gets replaced by honey which you eventually harvest.

5. CROWDING DOWN.

The methods described so far cannot be put to systematic use by a comb honey beekeeper because, with the exception of using package bees, each depends upon the swarming inclinations of the bees which are unpredictable and to some extent beyond the beekeeper's control. Still, in apiculture as in everything else, much of one's success depends upon seizing unexpected opportunities and making the best of them, rather than just laying down plans in advance and expecting nature always to cooperate.

While perfectly good comb honey, especially in shallow extracting frames instead of small sections, can be produced simply by supering normal colonies (6), it is not the way to get the best honey nor do you get very large crops. Bees are sometimes slow to enter supers containing no drawn comb, especially if these are furnished with small sections. To get them into the supers quickly and in large numbers, it is usually necessary to crowd them into them. This means reducing the hive to one story on its own stand. A colony intended for comb honey production should not be moved to a new stand, since this manipulation instantly deprives it of all the foraging bees—precisely the bees you need to store up your crop.

The best way to reduce the colony to a single story is to leave on the original stand whichever story contains the most brood, making sure the queen is there too. Two improvements over this simple splitting of the colony are possible, and almost always well worthwhile. One is to shake some or all of the bees from the combs that are not left there, and the other is to select, from each story of the original hive, those that are most nearly filled with *sealed* brood.

33

Suppose, for example, you have a strong colony in two stories which you wish to use to maximum effect for comb honey production. In fact, of course, you will probably have several such colonies in the apiary, so the procedure about to be described can be applied to any and all of these. You proceed as follows.

Set both stories off the hive stand and onto the hive cover nearby, the latter being upside down on the ground to minimize injury to the bees. Now remove all the combs from one of these, replacing only those that contain the most sealed brood. Remove similar combs from the other story, exchanging them for combs containing little or no brood, and put the hive body resulting from this procedure, and thus containing most advanced and sealed brood, back on its hive stand. Be sure, too, that the queen is with this part, so she remains on the original hive stand. Next shake all or most of the bees from the remaining combs in front of the hive containing the brood, to get a single story hive with most of the advanced brood and bees of the original colony. Over this colony put a queen excluder and at least two comb honey supers.

Two problems result from this procedure. The first is that you have on your hands a hive body filled with honey, pollen and mostly unsealed brood but few or no bees. It is quite vulnerable to being robbed out. The only thing you can do with it is add it to another hive, preferably one that is not terribly strong and in need of building up. Such a hive should have sufficient population to nurse the unsealed brood you are giving to it. There is no rule for this; you simply have to use judgment. In case you have in the apiary any colonies in single stories then you have here a perfect opportunity for building them to proper two story colonies at one stroke. A good solution to the problem, therefore, is to have prepared nucleus colonies (13) in single story hives to utilize in just this way. This does, however, result in increasing the number of colonies in your apiary, which you may or may not want. The only solution to that problem, if it is a problem, is to thus unite the extra stories to nucleus hives, then reunite these back to the comb honey producing hives after the comb honey harvest.

My friend Rev. Clarkson shows how he inserts foundation in split sections without tools, first moistening corners, then folding, and inserting a full sheet in four sections.

IIII➡

The second problem resulting from such hive reduction, which is sometimes a very taxing one, is that such crowding gives the bees a very strong inducement to build queen cells in preparation for swarming, thus threatening to depopulate the powerful honey-gathering colony which it was your purpose to create by this procedure. I believe that the only way to meet this problem is to have this colony headed by a young queen—one that is not over a year old—and give it plenty of super room right from the start. Pile on three supers if there is any chance of the bees occupying them all. Then cross your fingers and hope that the bees will busy themselves with honey gathering rather than building queen cells.

Some comb honey beekeepers at this point begin a systematic program of cutting out queen cells if they begin to appear, but I consider this to be folly. To do it, you must completely dismantle the hive below the excluder every week, shake the bees from each comb to make sure no cell is missed, and then destroy every one of them. This is not only messy and time consuming, but worse, it keeps the colony constantly demoralized and thus ineffective for honey getting.

6. RAISING COMB HONEY WITHOUT FUSS AND BOTHER.

Comb honey supers can be set on strong colonies in exactly the way one would add extracting supers, and without any special manipulations at all. One advantage of this uncomplex management is that it takes little time. If a beekeeper has only an hour or so to super up an apiary of perhaps twenty five colonies, before moving on to the next apiary, then he must adopt a system that enables him to do what he can, and in my own busy life I often find myself compelled to cut corners.

Another advantage of this simple practice is that it does not stimulate swarming unduly, as so many of the systems for raising comb honey do.

This method is particularly suitable for producing cut comb honey, or comb honey that is to be marketed in regular unwired extracting frames, since these supers are not essentially different from ordinary extracting supers. It is important to induce the bees to occupy them at once, however, which they are not likely to do when a super contains only foundation and no drawn comb. The two outermost frames of the super should, accordingly, be regular extracting frames, wired, and containing drawn comb.

Similarly, if section supers are put over a regular two story colony, then the first one, at least, should have a drawn bait section in the middle, saved over from the preceding season (16). This induces the bees to enter the supers at once, thereby reducing crowding in the hive below, and thereby also greatly reducing the tendency of the colony to swarm. Without bait sections, or a couple of drawn combs in the cut comb honey supers, the bees are likely to ignore the supers completely for two or three weeks or more and, in the meantime, swarm.

Finally, if you raise comb honey by this simple method of supering normal or unmanipulated colonies, choose only the strongest colonies for the purpose. In all comb honey production it is important to get the supers filled fast, so that the combs will be full and not darkened ("travel stained") by the long presence of bees in them (17). These things are not important in producing extracted honey.

7. CROWDING COLONIES DOWN WITH MINIMUM FUSS.

Cut comb honey or any other kind that is stored in regular shallow extracting frames can be produced over normal but strong colonies, without any special manipulations other than those that might normally be undertaken in producing extracted honey. Section honey, on the other hand, whether of the traditional square kind or the round sections, is best produced over colonies that have been reduced to a single story, thereby crowding the bees into the supers which they are sometimes otherwise reluctant to work in.

This crowding down always presents problems, the worst one being the stimulus to swarming as a result of overcrowding. A more immediate problem is what to do with the hive bodies, full of brood, pollen, honey and bees, which are left over as a result of this crowding of the bees down into one story. It is a problem that has no neat solution that I know of, unless one wants to increase the number of colonies he has. In that case the stories split off can simply be united with nucs (13, 14), whereupon they quickly build up to regular honey producing colonies.

One very easy way of effecting this reduction and crowding down of the colonies, without creating new problems, is simply to split each two-story colony in two, requeen the half that was thereby made queenless, and put a comb honey super on each half. Then after the honey is harvested the two halves can be reunited, with the young queens on top, thus improving the chance that they, rather

37

than the older queens, will survive to head the two-story colonies resulting from this manipulation. If this is done, then the story that is originally split off from the two story colony, prior to supering, must of course be set on a hive stand right next to the story that is left in place; otherwise, many foraging bees, returning to empty hive stands after the two halves are reunited, will be lost.

Of course the great drawback to this simple system is that it means trying to produce honey over *weak* colonies, in violation of one of the most basic principles of apiculture. One strong colony will normally store up far more honey than two, or even several, weak ones; and a hive that is simply split in two is certainly not strengthened. On the contrary, even if strong to begin with, it is thereby simply reduced to two relatively weak colonies.

Still, the method is simple, it brings about a fairly reliable requeening of one's entire apiary, and, unlike other methods of colony reduction, it does not precipitate swarming; on the contrary, it considerably inhibits it. I know one able comb honey beekeeper who follows this method routinely each year. Having made his splits and supered in the spring, just as his bees are beginning to think about swarming, he pretty much ignores them for the rest of the summer, until time to harvest his crop. He breaks no production records, but he certainly minimizes toil and trouble.

The simple method just described does involve one complication of course, and that is that you must have on hand an extra bottom board, cover and inner cover for each colony that is thus split. This, however, only means an extra investment in equipment; it does not mean much extra work. And two precautions must be heeded in carrying out this method. The first is to be sure that the queen stays with the story that remains on the original hive stand, the moved one being the one that is requeened. The reason for this is that it is very easy to requeen a colony that has lost its flying bees, as this one will have, the flying bees all going back to their original stand. And the other precaution is to leave whichever story is heavy with honey, in case either is, on the original stand, while making sure that the moved half has at least some honey. The reason for this is to reduce the likelihood that the bees remaining on their original stand will simply rob out the part that is moved. This is almost certain to happen when colonies are split late in the season, or when no honey flow is in progress, but it seldom happens when the colonies are building up rapidly in the spring. To further discourage such possible robbing, you can reduce the entrance of the moved half and plug it gently with grass, which will dry up and fall out in a few days, by which time the bees will have adapted themselves to the radical change you have imposed on them.

8. SHOOK SWARMING AND PADGENING.

All the orthodox methods of raising comb honey involve reducing a colony to a single story, usually from two stories, thereby deliberately crowding the bees and more or less forcing them into the supers. The greatest drawback in this system is that such crowding is a considerable goad to swarming, and if the colony swarms you have not only wasted your time, but virtually lost your comb honey crop as well. In addition to this, such manipulation is a bit of work, and you create a problem of what to do with the top story that was removed from the colony.

Those problems are entirely avoided by using good prime swarms hived on foundation as comb honey colonies, in the manner described (2, 3). Here, however, you have two quite different problems. One is that you do not know when or where you will be able to get such swarms, and the other is that, in the cases of natural swarms from your own hives, you are likely not to know which colonies they came from. There is, in short, too large an element of luck and chance in this method.

Might it not, then, be possible somehow to combine these two systems in such a way as to avoid the problems of both? Indeed it is. You simply create your own swarms, at times of your own choosing, and use them as you would natural prime swarms. This is quaintly called "shook" swarming, and it was once quite widely practiced as a means of swarm control.

To shook swarm a colony, you simply find one that you think is likely to swarm if left to itself—one which is very strong, for example, at the swarming season, or even one that has started building queen cells—and you *shake* most of the bees from the combs onto a cloth sheet or something of like nature. If the queen of that colony is run into a mailing cage and this suspended from a tripod a few inches above where the bees are shaken, then they will all cluster around her, and this swarm can be dealt with like any natural swarm. What you have gained from this manipulation, of course, is having a swarm at a time of your own choosing, and inducing it to cluster where you want it to cluster.

This cannot really be described as a means of swarm prevention, of course, because you in fact create a swarm. It is, however, obviously better than having the bees swarm at a time, and cluster at a place, of their choosing.

If in performing this shook swarm operation only about half or two-thirds of the bees from the parent hive are shaken from the combs, then that parent hive can be moved off to one side in the same apiary and the artificially created swarm hived in a new hive on the original stand of the parent colony. The result is the same as padgening, described above (4).

To apply the foregoing procedure to comb honey production, proceed as follows.

Select a strong colony, which may or may not be preparing to swarm by building queen cells. If unsealed queen cells are present, and you are nevertheless certain that the colony has not already thrown a natural swarm, so much the better. Now move this colony off its stand and in its place put a shallow extracting super fitted with nine frames of foundation only, no drawn comb, on top of which place a queen excluder, and on top of this three comb honey supers of whatever kind—section supers, rounds or cut comb supers, all of them, of course, fitted with foundation and ready for honey storage. Cover this with inner cover and regular hive cover.

Next shake most of the bees from the original colony onto a sheet in front of this shallow super, which is going to serve as a much reduced brood chamber. "Most of the bees" means roughly two-thirds of them, which in turn means giving each comb one vigorous downward shake, holding it vertically. Watch for the queen, and make certain she goes into the shallow hive with the other bees. It is not necessary to cage her. It is a good idea to snip her wing tips before she goes in, however, or, if you do not wish to do that, to slip a queen excluder *under* the shallow brood chamber after you are sure the queen has gone in, leaving it there for only a day or two. Either of these measures will prevent the bees from swarming out again the next day and absconding, which they are not likely to do, but which they sometimes do.

Having completed this shook swarming, set the parent hive back-to-back with the new shallow hive with comb supers, so that it is facing in the opposite direction, as described before (4). Requeen this colony, either by introducing a new queen or a ripe queen cell, or simply let them raise a new queen. It is very easy to get a colony which has been moved, as this one has, to accept a new queen, since all the foraging bees go back to their accustomed entrance, facing the other way, and enter the shallow super you have put there. After about a week or so, when this moved colony has settled down and adjusted to its new situation, and a few bees have started coming and going at the entrance, you should give them an extracting super; not a comb honey super, because the colony has become too depopulated to do a good job finishing comb honey. These bees will, however, usually put up two shallow supers of extracting honey before the season ends. You left all of its brood with it when you did the

40

shook swarming, so the colony recovers quite fast as this hatches out.

A shook swarm created in the manner just described and hived in a shallow super of foundation on the original stand of the parent colony will produce a fine crop of comb honey even, sometimes, under adverse conditions of weather or weak flows. Sometimes the results are fairly spectacular. About the only ways it can fail are, first, by creating an inadequate shook swarm, that is, by not shaking sufficient bees from the combs of the parent hive; or, second, by having the bees swarm from this new shallow hive. This is easily prevented in either of the two ways described, is not very likely to happen anyway, and is almost certain not to happen after the bees have been in this new hive for two nights. After that the colony can be more or less ignored, except to harvest the honey and add supers as needed.

When the main summer honey flows are over, and well in advance of fall, which would be by the first of August in my latitude, the last of the comb honey should be harvested. If supers remain unfinished, they should be given to another colony for finishing, and the shallow brood chamber that remains on the stand dealt with as follows.

Set the shallow brood chamber off to one side, replace it with the parent hive that was put back-to-back with it some weeks earlier, such that this parent hive is now exactly where it was, and facing the same way as it was, before the shook swarm operation was performed. And finally, unite the shallow brood chamber to this hive by the newspaper method (14) . The brood in it will now hatch out, it will become filled with honey, and be extracted along with the other extracting supers. That is why you used only nine frames of foundation when this shallow hive was set up, for ease of eventual extracting.

It is not a very great job to deal with eight or ten colonies in this manner, and thus raise perhaps a thousand or twelve hundred or more sections in one season, depending on the nature of the flows. Four supers of comb honey from each such hive, plus a couple of supers of extracting honey from the parent hives from which the bees are shaken, is a reasonable expectation, and much larger crops are common.

Package bees cannot be used in this fashion, because success depends on the principle of padgening (4), that is, upon having a strong force of foraging bees oriented to the stand where the shook swarm is established. Frames of drawn comb cannot be used in the shallow brood chamber, either, nor even one such frame, for if there

41

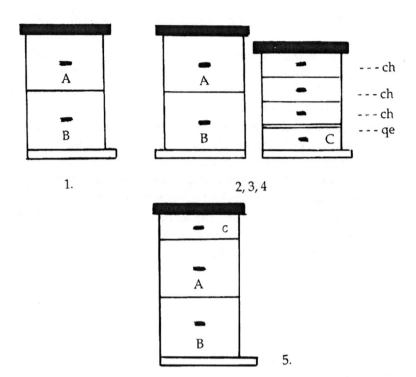

1.

2, 3, 4

--- ch
--- ch
--- ch
--- qe

5.

Shook swarming into a shallow super:

1. Select a strong colony (AB) that seems likely to swarm if preventative measures are not taken.

2. Set that colony immediately in back of its original stand, and facing in the opposite direction. In its place, on its original stand, place a shallow super (C) fitted with nine frames of foundation, on top of which put a queen excluder (qe) and three comb honey supers (ch).

3. Shake most of the bees from the parent hive (AB) in front of this shallow extracting super (C), including the queen, preferably clipped.

4. Requeen the parent hive (AB) on its new stand just behind its original stand or (less preferably) let them raise their own queen.

5. After the comb honey has been harvested, return the parent hive (AB) to its original stand, and facing as it was originally facing, and on top of it place the shallow extracting super (C) that has in the meantime served as a brood chamber. Foraging bees from the parent hive (AB) will find the entrance which has been turned around, the extra queen will be deposed, the brood from the shallow super (C) will all hatch out and be replaced by honey, which can be harvested.

These two colonies have been shook swarmed and parent hives placed on top of supers over double screen, with entrance in front for lower colony, in back for parent colony on top. Note shallow super on bottom.

is anything of this nature to make the shallow brood chamber more attractive to the bees than the supers, then they will simply make their nest down there and ignore the supers, defeating you.

9. RADICAL SHOOK SWARMING.

This procedure is exactly like the one just described (8), except that you shake all of the bees from the parent colony, and then distribute the frames of brood that are left over to other colonies. If, for example, the parent hive consisted of two stories, then you can give one of these, containing brood but devoid of bees, to some other colony in the apiary, and the other story to another.

This of course results in a somewhat larger shook swarm, but it is not so easy to deal with that shallow brood chamber after the comb honey harvest. In addition to this problem, you get some oversized hives in the apiary, by adding brood chambers to them, creating headaches for yourself later on.

10. DOUBLE SHOOK SWARMING.

A skilled and experienced apiarist, aiming to get a truly prodigious crop of comb honey from just a few colonies, may wish to undertake the double shook swarm method, which is an invention of the author. It should not be attempted by the inexperienced, because there are too many chances in it for error, but anyone who has used successfully the regular shook swarm method described before (8) will want to try this variation. It is a method for establishing, with a single operation, a two-queen colony of immense population, at the same time virtually eliminating any danger of swarming, which is so often the bane of the comb honey beekeeper.

The method of shook swarming into a shallow super (8) is a tried and true one, which has worked well for me and for most others I know of who have tried it. But by its very success it creates a problem for any comb honey beekeeper, and that is, that for every colony thus manipulated, you end up the season with an extra shallow extracting super, namely, the one that served as a shallow brood chamber for the comb honey hive. Even a beekeeper who goes in ex-

After honey is harvested from shook swarmed colonies, parent colonies are returned to original hive stands and shallow brood chambers united with them over newspaper. Vacated bottom boards indicate where parent colonies were placed during honey flow.

Special bottom board for use in double shook swarm system. Bees enter hive on either side rather than front end.

Below, divided hive body for use with double shook swarm systems.

tensively for raising extracted honey does not want constantly to be adding to his inventory of extracting supers, and one who is primarily a comb honey beekeeper is likely to need them even less. And to make matters somewhat worse, those extra extracting supers that accumulate are filled with very dark combs, having been used through an entire season for brood rearing. This fault is not grave, since darkened combs do not, in my opinion, damage or discolor the honey that is spun from them, but all the same, we prefer light extracting combs.

If, then, a way could be found of doing the shook swarming into a full-depth hive body fitted with frames of foundation, then that problem would be overcome. You would, indeed, end up the season with extra hive bodies of dark combs, but being full-depth ones, this would be no problem. Any beekeeper always has use for these. If he does not need them himself, then he can make up nucs with them, or hive swarms on them, and sell them to other beekeepers for a good price.

But here we get a new problem; namely, that if you shook swarm into a full-depth hive body, then you lose the great advantage of the shallow brood chamber, which is, that it forces more bees into the supers where you want them.

One might try to overcome both problems by shook swarming into a nuc box containing four or five full-depth frames, and then supering over that. Such a brood chamber would have about the same internal volume as a shallow extracting super used as a brood chamber, and it would utilize full-depth frames. It would never work as a means of raising comb honey, however, because bees do a very poor job of finishing comb honey in a super that is wider than their own brood chamber. There would also be some troublesome problems of carpentry.

Suppose, however, you were to divide a hive body lengthwise, with a sheet of quarter-inch plywood or masonite, put five frames of foundation on each side, then shook swarm bees into each side. By so doing you would in principle get double the result of shook swarming into a shallow super, and at the same time avoid all the problems outlined above. I have in fact used this system, and it does, indeed, result in immensely populated two-queen colonies that do not swarm, and in truly prodigious honey crops.

A double shook swarmed colony with entrances on each side and four round section supers.

More precisely, the manipulation is as follows.

Select two adjacent strong colonies. Both requirements are important, namely, that they be strong, and closely adjacent to each other, preferably no more than a foot apart. (All my hive stands are made to hold two colonies, so virtually all my hives are closely adjacent to others). Find, in each colony, the comb that has the queen on it, and set this off to one side in a shaded place, out of the way. Next set each colony off to one side, and midway between where they were both standing put a bottom board constructed in such a way that there is an entrance on each side, rather than in the front end. On this bottom board put a full-depth hive body that is divided right down the middle lengthwise by a piece of quarter-inch stock. Put five (not less) full-depth frames of foundation on each side of that divider, and over the whole hive body put a queen excluder and at least four comb honey supers. The hive should now be such that no bees can pass back and forth between the two chambers of the hive *except* through the hive entrances on either side, or up and down through the excluder. This will insure that while the bees can mingle freely in the supers, and within the two chambers of the brood chamber, the queens cannot pass back and forth or come into contact with each other.

Now, having gotten that divided brood chamber set up, shake the bees from one of the parent hives on a cloth at the side entrance facing where that hive was hitherto sitting, letting the queen, which you set off to one side, run into the hive with them about midway along in the shook swarm operation. Then do exactly the same with the other parent hive, on the other side of the double chambered brood chamber. Meanwhile, before running the queens in, it is a good idea to snip off the tips of their wings, as noted before (2).

Now stop to consider the result of all this. What you have is a full-depth divided hive body, into each side of which you have hived a swarm. The queens cannot mingle with each other, so each is safe from the other. The other bees mingle peacefully, because they all enter this double hive more or less together, and swarms thus thrown together, *before* one of them takes over a hive, do not fight. If you were to shook swarm bees into one side on one day, and then try to shook swarm another colony into the other side on another day, then the two swarms would *not* unite, but would more or less kill each other off; but the method here described avoids this.

Each queen now begins laying in the half of the brood chamber that is hers, so you have a fine two-queen colony set up. The bees, having little room for honey storage below, immediately go to work in the supers, and continue working in them to produce

Two prime swarms were hived simultaneously into a divided hive body with an entrance on each side, and immediately occupied all three comb honey supers.

a huge crop of honey for you. The hive is likely to have seven or eight comb honey supers all filled or filling up with honey before long, depending on how good the flows are.

Normally, as soon as the shook swarm operation is completed, the bees that were in the hive to the right will begin using the entrance to the new hive that is on the right side, and those that were in the hive to the left will begin using the new entrance on the left, but there may be some confusion here for a day or two. Sometimes the bees tend to drift more to one side than the other. This can be corrected by turning the hive somewhat, so as to favor the less used entrance, until you have the bees using both entrances in approximately equal numbers. Actually, this is not a serious problem, since the bees all store honey in the same supers; but if they favor one entrance over the other, then the brood nest on that side quickly becomes congested, while the brood nest on the other side falls behind.

The parent hives from which the bees were shook swarmed should of course be padgened; that is, simply set up on new hive stands in the same apiary, requeened and supered (4). The field forces of these two hives join the shook swarms on the original stand, thus eliminating any swarming from the parent colonies, which in turn recover quickly and put up a fair crop of extracting honey for you.

After the summer honey flows, early in August, the last of the comb honey can be harvested from the two-queen hive and any unfinished sections given to other colonies to complete.

There then remains the question of what to do with the double brood chamber enormously populated with bees but almost totally devoid of honey, this having all gone into the comb honey supers.

Two good solutions to this problem are available. One is simply to remove the divider, thus creating a normal brood chamber, and add another story of drawn combs. This will work provided you can count on a sufficient fall flow for the colony to gather adequate winter stores. The extra queen will, of course, be deposed by the bees themselves.

The other solution is to unite this brood chamber, with or without its divider, to another colony by the newspaper method (14), then use it in the spring to make nucs or to establish a new colony. This latter solution reduces, of course, the possibility of winter loss. It means probably losing both queens, but both are likely to be older queens anyway.

There is probably no better way than by this double shook swarm manipulation to obtain very large comb honey crops from one or a few colonies. It involves a considerable manipulation, but it is not very time consuming when done by a skilled beekeeper. Probably the only real drawback is that, with two queens and in fact two distinct colonies involved in a single operation, the chances of something going wrong are considerably increased. It is for this reason that it should not be tried by beginners, and certainly not by anyone having only three or four colonies of bees.

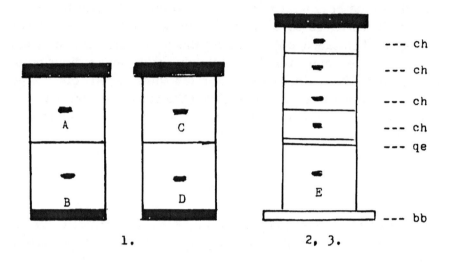

1.   2, 3.

Double shook swarming into a divided hive:

　　1. Select two strong colonies (AB and CD) closely adjacent to each other, and move them to a new location in the same apiary.

　　2. In their place, and midway between where they were, place a bottom board having an entrance on each side and no entrance in front (bb), and on this place a full depth hive body (E) divided lengthwise through the middle and fitted with ten full-depth frames of foundation. On this place a queen excluder (qe) and four comb honey supers (ch) and cover.

　　3. Shake most of the bees, including the queen, preferably clipped, from hive (AB) into the side of the new hive (E) which faces towards where (AB) originally stood. Do the same with hive (CD) into the other side of the new hive (E).

　　4. Requeen the parent hives (AB) and (CD) on their new stands or, less preferably, let them raise their own queens.

　　5. After the comb honey has been harvested, unite the new hive (E) to other colonies in the apiary for overwintering, or supply it with a super of honey to overwinter where it is, either with or without removing the divider in it.

50

11. REDUCING THE COLONY AND LETTING THE BEES RAISE A NEW QUEEN.

A very effective method of reducing the honey producing hive to a single story without immediately stimulating the impulse to swarm is to temporarily deprive it of a queen. This procedure has the advantage of relative simplicity over some of the others described, and it can be combined with some of the principles already discussed as follows.

When you think the swarming period is about to begin, and preferably before any queen cells have been begun in the colony you want to reduce, remove eight combs containing mostly sealed brood together with some honey and pollen from that colony, together with adhering bees, but *without* the queen. Check each of the eight combs carefully to be sure the queen is not on one of them or, if you see her, pluck her gently from the comb and let her crawl into a part of the hive that has been set aside, so that she will not end up in the reduced colony. Put those eight combs of mostly sealed brood into a hive body and then add, more or less in the center of this hive body, one comb of mostly *unsealed* brood and bees, making sure that it contains at least some worker eggs, but no queen. The presence of eggs ensures that there is or will be young larvae from which the bees can develop a new queen.

Set this hive, with eight combs of mostly sealed brood, one comb with eggs and larvae, and adhering bees but no queen, onto a bottom board and then back onto the colony's regular stand, add a queen excluder and at least two comb honey supers, and covers.

That reduced but queenless colony will immediately become very strong, first by the automatic addition to it of the entire field force of the original colony, since all these field bees return to their accustomed stand, and then by the addition of the thousands of worker bees emerging from the combs. It can be made stronger still, if you wish, by shaking some of the bees (but not the queen!), from the combs that are to remain with the other hive, in front of this reduced colony, although you should not overdo this, since bees are needed in that other colony to tend the unsealed brood left there.

This reduced colony will not swarm, at least for awhile, because it has no queen. The bees immediately start raising a new queen from larvae on the single comb of unsealed brood.

Meanwhile, all the rest of the colony, which contains the original queen, is given a bottom board and cover and set back-to-back behind this reduced colony. It looses its field force to the reduced colony, of course, but it soon rebuilds its population and becomes a normal colony.

As the supers on the reduced colony begin to fill with honey, more supers are added. They normally will fill rapidly, since there is not much unsealed brood in this hive for the bees to feed, and you will need to be alert to the need to add supers. Of course the size of the crop will depend on the strength of the honey flow. With a decent flow, the crop can be very large indeed and, coming in fast, the sections get filled very well, and the cappings stay white until the harvest.

When the early honey flows taper off, you should harvest all the supers, and reunite the two colonies by simply setting the one that was placed in back of the reduced colony back on that reduced colony, and facing forwards. The bees will be slightly confused by this sudden change of their entrance location, but that will last only a day or two. And of course the reunited colonies will now have two queens, but one of these will sooner or later disappear.

Some beekeepers maintain that, when queenright colonies are united, the queen that has the best chance of surviving is (a) the younger queen, or (b) the queen in the upper stories. I have never tested these beliefs, but I think there is probably some truth in them. You might, accordingly, wish to set the reduced colony, with its younger queen, on top of the other, having both on the original hive stand facing forwards, that is, facing the way they faced before the division into two colonies was undertaken.

Two additional points need to be made about this method.

The first is, that while swarming is delayed in the reduced colony by the fact of its queenlessness, it must be remembered that this queenlessness is temporary. Within a week this powerful colony will have queen cells well underway, and just as soon as one of these is capped over, which will be in about ten days, the bees will have an inclination to swarm, even though they have no laying queen. Therefore, you should, about a week after reducing the colony, inspect the one comb that contains queen cells and destroy all but one. Actually this is not difficult, since there should be no queen cells on any comb except this one. And you will need to destroy extra cells only once, since the bees will not have any more young larvae to convert to queens. Hence this inspection really involves little more than the removal, just once, of one comb. It will be well, however, to glance at the other eight combs, to be sure there were no eggs or young larvae in these from which queen cells might have been started.

And the second point is that this reducing procedure should be timed, as nearly as possible, to coincide with the beginning of a honey flow, for your object is to get comb honey supers filled as quickly as possible. If you undertake this procedure just at about the time the swarming season is starting or about to start, then that will, in most beekeeping localities, also be about the beginning of a honey flow from the early sources, so it should work out about right.

This method does undoubtedly work, and the beekeeper is saved the expense of buying a new queen. The method was first described to me by Mr. Vic Blazevic, a Virginia beekeeper who picked it up from Mr. Otis Poss, of Maryland.

PART III:
THINGS TO DO

Sweet Clover

INTRODUCTION

Many of the tasks that fall to the comb honey beekeeper are just things any good beekeeper must do, whereas others are unique to the comb honey beekeeper's special craft. What I try to do in the pages that follow is offer suggestions with respect to the problems that almost any comb honey beekeeper must deal with, omitting, where I can, those that are simply a part of beekeeping itself. I do not, for example, set forth methods of swarm control, except insofar as these are incidental to some particular system of management for comb honey. *My How-to-Do-It Book of Beekeeping*, which has been considerably revised and enlarged since its first edition, offers as complete a system of apiculture, in all its aspects, as I am able to compose, and I try here to repeat no more than necessary what is said there. A few things said in that book are absolutely basic to comb honey beekeeping, however, and thus are included here. An example is the newspaper method of uniting colonies, which is certainly one of the simplest and most elementary of all apicultural manipulations. It would be impossible to be a comb honey beekeeper very long without performing this manipulation.

Dandelion

12. HOW TO LOCATE YOUR COMB HONEY APIARY.

Finding a place to locate any comb honey apiary is usually not hard. It should preferably be near where you live, since you need to visit a comb honey apiary more frequently than apiaries used for getting extracted honey, and it should be where you can keep an eye on it to prevent vandalism. If you locate it near neighbors, then it should also be out of their sight, to minimize their fear of stings.

Comb honey beekeeping lends itself perfectly to what is called back lot beekeeping; that is, to having a small apiary near your house. Such an apiary can also be located on a rooftop very nicely. The best comb honey apiary I ever had consisted of about a dozen hives on the flat roof of my garage, in the heart of a populous city. Many basswoods grew along the streets and in the park, and my bees had no competition there from other apiaries.

A rooftop comb honey apiary in the heart of the city

13. HOW TO PREPARE NUCS.

When two-story colonies are reduced to a single story, as a means of crowding the bees into the section comb honey supers, then the very best use that can be made of the extra story that is taken from each such colony is to combine it with a nucleus colony, or nuc, thereby establishing a new colony. About the only alternatives to this, really, are either to add these extra stories to existing normal colonies, thereby creating abnormally tall colonies that are inefficient honey producers, or else pile these extra stories on top of each other on a hive stand, three or four stories high, and cover them, thereby creating new abnormally high colonies that will be headaches to deal with later on.

It is an exceedingly simple matter to make up a nuc. Simply take three frames of bees and brood from any colony, or indeed from the extra story that you remove from your comb honey colony when you reduce it to one story, place these three combs next to each other in the center of a hive body, introduce a new queen, and then fill the rest of the hive body up with drawn combs. Be sure there is some honey and pollen in those three frames of brood. Reduce the entrance, and plug it loosely with grass to confine the bees and keep out robber bees for a few days.

Some beekeepers construct simple little nuc boxes, just large enough to hold from three to five such combs. But if you are going to use the nucs to start new colonies, using the extra story from reduced comb honey colonies, as suggested here, then they might far better be started in regular hive bodies to begin with, since they will eventually end up in such hive bodies.

In uniting the extra stories to these nucs, you should observe the following: If the nuc contains drawn combs, in addition to the three combs of brood, then the extra story from the comb honey colony can go either on top of it or under it, with a sheet of newspaper between the two. But if the nuc contains any frames of foundation only, then it must go on top of the other story. Foundation, as a general principle, must always be drawn out upstairs in a hive, not down below, where it will be damaged and chewed by the bees.

This means of utilizing the extra stories from reduced comb honey colonies results, of course, in an expansion of the apiary, which you might not particularly want. The increase in the number of colonies is not as great as may at first seem, however, for the comb honey colonies, that were reduced to one story each plus supers, can be united with each other after the comb honey has been harvested, thereby reducing the number of these colonies to half what they were. Thus the increase resulting from one manipulation

Making up nucs

is somewhat compensated for by the reduction resulting from another.

The foregoing remarks, incidentally, illustrate a feature of beekeeping, as an agricultural pursuit, that should be appreciated; namely, that the expansion or reduction of one's enterprise is quite simple and easy. In most other branches of agriculture, such expansion and reduction are likely to involve the purchase or sale of lands and buildings, which is usually not easy.

Basswood

14. HOW TO UNITE NUCS AND COLONIES BY THE NEWSPAPER METHOD.

The newspaper method of uniting colonies is one of the simplest and best known of all apicultural manipulations, and will already be known to most readers, but since many of the systems of management I describe utilize this manipulation at one point or another, it will be desirable to describe it.

Any two normal colonies, or parts of colonies, or nucleus colonies, can be united into one as follows: Remove cover and inner cover from one, lay a newspaper over the top of it, poke a couple of holes in the paper with a hive tool, then simply set the other colony or part of a colony over this. The bees chew through the newspaper so that not a trace remains and, thus mingling gradually, they unite peacefully.

This method of uniting colonies does not work, however, in the fall, after cool weather has settled in and the bees have begun to settle into their winter torpor. They are likely to remain as two distinct colonies, one of which will be dead in the spring.

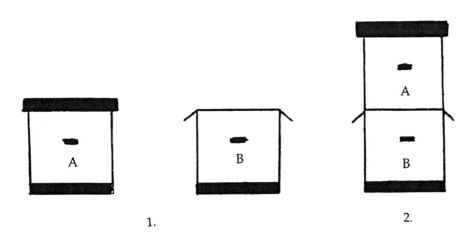

1. 2.

Uniting colonies: Replace the cover and inner cover of one colony (B) with a sheet of newspaper, then set the other colony (A) over this. By the time the bees have chewed through the paper, the disposition to conflict will have abated.

15. HOW TO GET A LITTLE STRAINED HONEY WITHOUT MUCH EQUIPMENT.

It is very difficult to raise comb honey exclusively. Sometimes you will end up with imperfect sections that you will want to cut up and pack as chunk honey. To do this you need some strained honey with which to fill up the jar. Sometimes you will have on hand, at the end of the season, some combs that are improperly or incompletely capped over, even though the honey in them is ripe. The only thing to do with it is separate it from the combs and use it as strained honey. And besides this, comb honey cannot be used for cooking and baking, so a comb honey beekeeper will need some strained honey for his own use.

The obvious solution is to buy a tiny hand crank extractor. Even someone who produces comb honey on a large scale, as many as several hundred supers each year, needs nothing more by way of an extractor, since this represents a minor aspect of his work The danger here is not in getting too small an extractor, but in getting one that is too large—large enough, that is, to lead one more or less inadvertently into additional equipment and the commercial production of extracted honey. There is of course nothing wrong with that, provided you know what you are getting into. What we are talking about is something quite different, however, and that is raising comb honey.

A backlot comb honey beekeeper needs no extractor at all. To get the strained honey he needs, and to utilize culled comb honey, all he needs is a clean hive body with an all wire queen excluder nailed to the bottom. He then saves broken and otherwise imperfect sections and cut combs, dumps them into this box, and mashes them up with a clean stick. The honey crushed from the combs, which is sure to be of the very highest quality, is collected in a large pan underneath. There you have an "extractor" that costs almost nothing. The honey can be left in a warm room for a day or two and then strained through a nylon stocking.

The crushed combs will still contain quite a lot of honey, even after they have been draining in this box in a warm room for a week. To recover this, and at the same time salvage the valuable beeswax, dump the crushed combs into a clean and topless sixty-pound can, and submerge this in water heated to about 160°F. Do not under any circumstances put such a vessel containing beeswax or honey directly over heat, without the water bath, as this will risk igniting the wax, and certainly ruin the honey. When the wax has all melted, the container can be lifted from the hot water bath, allowed to cool, and the cake of wax lifted off. The honey thus salvaged can be used for baking and cooking. It can also be used very well for packing chunk honey, provided it has not been overheated, as it will be slow to granulate.

16. HOW TO GET BAIT SECTIONS.

Bait sections are simply standard or round sections that are partly drawn out but which contain no honey. They are obtained by letting your bees rob dry your unfinished comb honey supers in the previous fall. Their use, as the name suggests, is to attract or "bait" the bees up into comb honey supers. Bees tend to ignore foundation until they actually need it, but if they find a partly drawn comb their impulse is to finish drawing it out. They assume, so to speak, that work has begun in a super containing such a comb, and that it should therefore now proceed to completion

Bait sections, when finished, are not of as good quality as those finished quickly from foundation, their main fault being that they are somewhat more waxy. They are perfectly acceptable, however, and usually attractive in appearance. If you happen to have a few entire supers saved from the previous year, all or most of whose sections are partly drawn out, then these can be given to the bees to finish. They are, in fact, filled with bait sections. This finishing up of partially drawn supers is not recommended when using square wooden sections, as these will be excessively stained and propolized by being put twice on the hives, but it works fairly well with round section supers. It should be stressed, however, that this is at best a solution to a problem. It does not result in the best quality comb honey.

17. HOW TO PREVENT TRAVEL STAIN.

Travel stain is the darkening of the cappings of comb honey as a result of the bees walking over it. It is in no sense a mark of impurity, since it consists simply of the minute traces of propolis and resins that are perfectly clean and normally present in any hive. It is merely damaging to the appearance of the honey.

Whenever comb honey falls short of being snow white, it is almost certain to be the result either of travel stain or of the fact that some bees leave no air space between the cappings and the honey underneath. This latter is idiosyncratic to some colonies. It makes no difference at all how extracting honey is capped over, of course, but when comb honey is capped without the usual tiny air space underneath, then it is not quite as pretty.

A slight travel strain on comb honey is no real fault, unless you intend to enter it in a honey show, in which case it will be marked down. A small amount of travel stain simply alters the color of the cappings from snow white to light yellow, which is by no means unattractive. And I have in fact seen customers select comb honey that was heavily travel stained, remarking that they preferred dark honey. Travel stain is not, therefore, in my opinion a serious problem; though it is of course worth some effort to avoid it. If I were to choose between a delicious honey that was travel stained, and a bland clover-like honey that was snow white, I would certainly prefer the former, and so, I have found, would most of my customers.

The way to minimize travel stain is, of course, to get the supers filled quickly, and then get them harvested as soon as they are filled.

One fairly common management practice that greatly promotes travel stain is inserting a comb honey super between supers already occupied by the bees—between extracting supers, for example—or, worse yet, between the two stories of the hive itself. This is sometimes done in the effort to get the bees working in the comb honey super as quickly as possible. It is probably the worst way there is to achieve that result, because of the discoloration of the honey that results. A far better way to get bees into the supers, without that result, is to use a few bait sections (16).

18. HOW TO KEEP POLLEN OUT OF COMB HONEY.

The way to keep the bees from stuffing pollen into some of the cells of comb honey is, as noted elsewhere (37), to set comb honey supers on hives *over* honey. Bees normally store pollen in combs over brood, but *under* honey, so if there is honey in the top of a hive when the supers are added, then pollen is not likely to appear in them.

The trouble is, of course, that this condition cannot be met when comb honey is raised by any of the shook swarm methods described above. Those methods require supering over hives, usually very shallow ones, containing no drawn combs, and hence no honey at all.

Thus pollen in the supers, especially the bottom super, is sometimes a problem with these methods. I have found no satisfactory solution to it, but have noted that the problem is minimal when there is a good honey flow in progress.

There is, however, a market for comb honey containing plugs of pollen; namely, persons dedicated to using only natural foods. Pollen is a nutritious substance, and such persons sometimes place great value on it. They are therefore happy to buy comb honey containing pollen, but they must, of course, be warned that it is likely to have a strong and disagreeable taste.

This double shook swarmed hive produced eight supers of comb honey in a very poor season, most of it from a brief basswood flow.

19. HOW TO SUPER UP FOR COMB HONEY.

Almost every discussion of comb honey in the literature of apiculture gives quite precise and elaborate instructions with respect to the order and arrangement of the supers as they go one by one over the hive, these instructions being accompanied by a series of drawings. Invariably you are told to add super #2 over #1, when ready, then to shift these two with each other when #3 goes on, then switch #3 to the bottom when #4 goes on, and so forth. The whole procedure seems quite esoteric, and I am quite sure that not many comb honey beekeepers adhere very closely to this ritual or, in fact, even give much thought to it.

The underlying principle of supering is perfectly simple. It rests on the fact that bees work first and fastest in the bottom super. Therefore, when the bees are working well in the first super, give them another. When the first is nearly finished and they are working

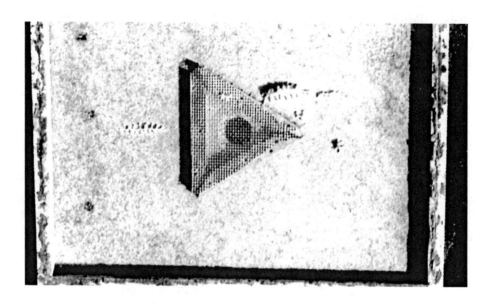

Triangular escapes are simple, easy to make and they work well.

The two-way bee escape should be used with a screen, not with an inner cover.

in the second, give them a third one, underneath the two already there. The basic, and very simple, principal to adhere to is this: Supers most nearly finished are always moved to the top, and those that have been least worked always go to the bottom. Thus, each new super rests right on the hive, all the others, of whatever degree of completion, going over this.

This arrangement, with the most advanced super on top and the least advanced on the bottom, has the effect of continuously drawing the bees up into the unfinished supers. The other advantage, which is a very big one, is that you can tell at a glance, just by checking the top super, whether it is ready for harvesting. If it is not ready, then neither are any of those underneath it, and when it is ready, then it can be harvested without any manipulation or disturbance of the supers below. When you take that top super, however, you are quite likely to discover that the one immediately underneath it is ready for harvesting too.

20. HOW TO HARVEST COMB HONEY.

Beekeepers have devised various means of clearing supers of bees, including repellent fumes, motor-driven blowers and various types of bee escapes. My own strong preference is for bee escapes, as they are simple, effective and cheap. Their only disadvantage is that it takes a couple of days for the bees to clear the supers, thus requiring a second trip to the apiary, but this is no significant problem when the apiary is nearby.

The type of escape that has been in use longest is the two-way Porter bee escape, and these work very well. The spring wires in them become gummed with beeswax after two or three uses, but this can be removed easily with a small nail or piece of wire, or the escape can be dipped into boiling water for a few minutes.

In recent years there has come into use a triangular bee escape, which works very well. The advantages of these are that they are easy to make, and there are no spring wires to get gummed up with beeswax. The principle on which they work is utterly simple: The bees, having left the super through the corners of the triangle, do not have enough sense to re-enter it by the same route, but instead try to go directly through the wire screen. Some beekeepers construct these simple escape boards by making two triangles, one inside the other, which further confuses the bees if they try to re-enter the supers. In any case, if you undertake to make escape boards of this type, you can use plywood of whatever thickness is at hand, bore a hole of about the size of a half-dollar in the middle, tack on the strips (about a quarter-inch thick) to make the triangle,

Harvesting comb honey supers using an escape screen.

and affix eight-mesh screen (not fly screen) to it. Additionally, the board must have a rim, of whatever thickness, on *both* sides.

The two-way Porter bee escape was designed to be used in the standard inner cover, but this is a great mistake. The inner cover that is on the supers about to be harvested must not be removed, for the reason about to be given, and, in any case, what you need is an escape *screen* under the supers, not an inner cover. For some unknown reason the bees vacate the supers much faster when screens are used. I believe that the honey is also less likley to damage from moisture, in case of rain, if separated from the bees below by a screen rather than by an inner cover.

An escape screen is not much different from a standard inner cover, except that much of its surface is eight-mesh screen rather than wood, and it has a shallow rim on both sides rather than one side only. Some beekeepers like to fit such screens with *two* escape devices, believing that the bees will vacate the supers twice as fast, but in fact one seems to work just as well as two.

Whichever method is used, whether it be the screen with the two-way escape or the simple triangular escape, it is essential *not* to loosen the inner cover that is on the supers to be harvested. The bees will have plastered it down tight with propolis, and thus it should remain. If loosened, then the bees are apt to find a way to re-enter the supers through some crack thus created, and they will begin to rob the honey from them.

Thus you should not ascertain whether a super is ready for harvest by removing the inner cover to see. Instead, lift the super from underneath. Its weight will tell you how far along it is, or, if there is any doubt, you can peer into it from underneath. If, as recommended, (61), you have kept the most advanced super on top, then this will be the one most likely to be ready for harvesting and, upon prying it up from the one below, you will see at a glance whether that one is also ready for harvest.

To use an escape device, of either kind, simply slide the supers to be harvested back about an inch or so, tilt them up and, while balancing them in that position with one hand, slide the escape screen under with the other, then lower the supers onto the screen in such a way as to achieve a tight fit. This is quickly and easily accomplished using a hive tool. It is a needless and tiring waste of energy to lift the supers from the hive, set them aside, then lift them back on.

You can thus insert escape screens under all the supers in the apiary that are ready for harvest in just a few minutes, leaving the outer covers off the hives for the time being. Scraps of asphalt shingle work perfectly for covering the inner cover holes thus exposed, as these can be pressed down for a snug fit. Bees still on the inner covers can be smoked or brushed off. Then, before replacing the outer covers, check each hive to be sure no holes or cracks remain through which the bees could gain re-entry. Any such opening can be plugged with a bit of newspaper, and masking tape can be used to seal off any cracks. It is not necessary to use expensive duct tape for this.

The supers will usually be fairly clear of bees the next day, but it is probably better to wait two days before taking the supers, to get them entirely, or almost entirely, clear of bees. They can be left longer, but it is best to get the supers off the hives fairly soon, to minimize the chance of robbing and to prevent possible damage to the honey from moisture, in case of heavy rain. This latter is not a serious danger, and does not warrant anxiety in case it does rain.

Usually only one super per hive will be harvested at a time, but sometimes you will be harvesting two. In this case it is important not to separate the two. The two cannot be tilted up to insert the screen underneath if they have been separated (for the top one would slide off) and, more important, separating them is likely to create a crack through which the bees can re-enter and rob.

Sometimes you will find bees still in the supers when you return to the apiary to remove them. A dozen or so bees are not significant. These will fly to the nearest window in the honey house and can then be released. But if there are many bees still in the supers, then the explanation is one or more of the following: (1) There is brood above the escape device. Bees absolutely will not abandon brood. (2) The queen got trapped above the escape. Bees are reluctant to abandon their queen. This however, is rarely the explanation, as the queen is almost always in the brood nest. (3) The super to be harvested is too near to the brood nest. This is likely to be true in case you are harvesting a super over a single-story hive, but in any case, when there is brood directly beneath a super, then the bees will not vacate unless *two* escape devices, one on top of the other, are used, which usually solves the problem completely. (4) The escape device is itself obstructed. This is the first thing one suspects, of course, but it is seldom the correct explanation, and almost never happens with the triangular escape. (5) There is broken burr comb in the super, so that honey is exposed. Bees are slow to evacuate a super that has drizzles of honey. It is of course almost impossible to pry a super loose without breaking burr comb and thus creating some stickiness, but this is seldom a problem.

21. HOW TO DEAL WITH CULLED SECTIONS.

Nothing is perfect, and a comb honey beekeeper at the end of a honey flow always has some unfinished sections, or damaged ones, or frames not properly capped over.

There are usually people who are very fond of comb honey who are willing to buy these up, unlabeled, at perhaps half price, for their own use. But beyond that, the best way of using them is to cut them up into small irregular chunks, without making any attempt at uniform size or shape, and pack them as chunk honey in small jars. I use small wide-mouth jars that hold twelve ounces of honey for this purpose, and they solve the problem completely.

The reasons for using small jars for this purpose are, first, because the honey is consumed more quickly, before it has time to granulate, and second, because the comb honey can be cut into small irregular sizes and shapes without detracting from its appearance in such a jar.

22. HOW TO CONTROL WAX WORMS IN COMB HONEY.

The wax worms that attack comb honey are much smaller than the big, white, fast moving wax worms that attack brood combs. They are the larvae of the lesser wax moth, appropriately so called. They are so small that they are almost invisible at first. They

The species of wax worm that attacks comb honey is much smaller than that usually found in hives. Adult and pupal stages are here compared with a dime.

riddle the cappings with pin holes making them completely worthless.

Standard instructions for combating these tiny worms are to fumigate the supers, bisulfide being the usual fumigant. Like most fumigants, however, this one is foul smelling. It is also dangerous and highly flammable.

There is a much better and simpler way, and that is to subject the finished comb honey to near-zero (F.) temperatures for several hours. This is totally effective and harmless to the honey. More precisely, proceed as follows.

Place the comb honey in strong plastic bags, tightly sealed, of the kind sold for lining wastebaskets. The plastic bags used by grocery stores for bagging groceries work very well too, provided they are large enough so that the opening can be closed tight with a twist band. I use these, putting twelve sections in each. This must be done after the honey has been packed, of course; that is, after the two covers have been put on. The bags of sections are then put into a freezer that has already been running long enough to have become cold and left there until the temperature drops to near-zero (F.). Five degrees above zero is probably cold enough to destroy even the eggs

Comb honey should be bagged in plastic before being put in the freezer, to prevent condensation of moisture when it is taken out.

but the colder the better. Put a regular room thermometer into the freezer with the honey. A day or two should be enough to get down to the needed temperature. Then remove the bags of honey and leave them closed until they have returned to room temperature, which takes another day or two.

The reason for using plastic bags is, of course, to protect the honey against moisture. If sections of honey are removed from a freezer without this protection, then a heavy frost forms on them almost at once, then eventually melts, threatening considerable damage. Plastic bags completely overcome this danger.

Since there is a constant procession of comb honey into and out of the freezer, a very large quantity can be thus dealt with even with a small freezer. Even the freezer of an ordinary kitchen refrigerator will handle a considerable crop, provided the temperature can be reduced to below zero. If it cannot be made that cold, then the honey should not be put into it for a few days after harvesting, to ensure that any wax worm eggs have hatched.

Merely reducing the temperature of comb honey below freezing (32°F.), as recommended in some books, is not sufficient to destroy the egg stage of the wax moth. The near-zero temperature is effective against every stage, however, including the eggs. Since, however, it is the tiny worms themselves that are most vulnerable to this treatment, it is my own practice to wait three or four days before subjecting the honey to this cold treatment, to give any eggs a chance to hatch out. The larvae themselves are not easily visible in their early stage.

Round sections appear to be particularly vulnerable to damage by the lesser wax moth, probably because of all the interstitial spaces in the supers which are inaccessible to the bees, and which therefore provide perfect hiding places for the moths.

The presence of the lesser wax worms can usually be determined, even when the larvae themselves cannot be seen, by the frass or small accumulations of powdery beeswax here and there.

Though I have heard beekeepers express skepticism concerning the effectiveness of this freezer method, I can declare that, of the thousands of sections of honey that I have treated in this way over several years, not one has ever shown damage by wax worms, whereas, without such treatment, nearly half of them show such damage.

23. HOW TO DEAL WITH MOISTURE IN COMB HONEY.

Carl E. Killion, the great Illinois beekeeper and authority on comb honey production, devotes almost an entire chapter of his *Honey in the Comb* to the problem of comb honey damaged by moisture. He relates how, before he got this problem solved, he had been obliged sometimes to discard hundreds of supers of otherwise beautiful comb honey, now ruined by moisture. His solution was to use a dehumidifier in the room where the supers were stored.

Of the many thousands of comb honey sections I have raised, I have never had one damaged by moisture. This has been true even when rain has set in after I had inserted the escape screens, and the supers of comb honey were therefore still on the hives, but empty of bees, for several days of wet weather. It is not, therefore, a necessary problem of comb honey production. Perhaps it depends somewhat on geographical location, though my own area is not particularly known for dryness. I have speculated that if one crowds bees into the supers, and then gives them only one comb honey super at a time, which is the method described by Mr. Killion, then this might induce the bees to fill the limited super space with nectar a bit too fast, and cap the honey over too quickly, before it has time to evaporate completely; but this is purely speculative conjecture. My own practice is to put more than one super over colonies that have been reduced to limited brood rearing space, which certainly provides more space within the hive and enables the bees to evaporate fresh nectar better.

If humidity and thin honey are a problem then it can, in any case, be dealt with in the manner Mr. Killion suggests, namely, by the installation of a dehumidifier. These appliances are not expensive, and often useful for purposes unconnected with honey storage.

24. HOW TO REUSE CULLED SECTIONS WITHOUT FOUNDATION.

Unfilled sections can be returned to the bees to finish, provided more honey flows are anticipated. Otherwise, the capped comb in them can be cut out and marketed in small wide-mouth jars as chunk honey, as previously described (21), or consumed at home.

Usually the bees cap over the center of a section first, leaving a considerable edge uncapped. In this case, then it is the capped over center that is cut out for use, then the section can be returned to the bees *as is*, that is, without foundation, and they will refill it perfectly—provided, of course, there is a decent flow of nectar.

25. HOW TO COPE WITH GRANULATION.

One of the chief problems of raising comb honey is that there is no way to restore it to its original form once it has granulated. Warming it does not work, even if the temperature is kept below the melting point of the cappings.

There are, however, several things one can do to minimize this problem to the point where it is not a serious one .

In the first place, comb honey is slower to granulate than unprocessed liquid honey. The reason for this seems to be that particles from the air, falling on exposed honey, precipitate granulation.

Moreover, some honeys, especially tree honeys, are slow to granulate, so if comb honey is gathered from these sources there is no real problem. One of my own main honey flows is basswood, and it is usually the main source of my comb honey crop. This honey almost never granulates, even when stored for weeks in a cold honey house. Sections that are finished up on the fall flow, however, which is mainly goldenrod, are apt to granulate within a month if I don't get them sold.

Honey that is kept in a warm room, where it is warm day and night, is slow to granulate. The most rapid granulation occurs at

74

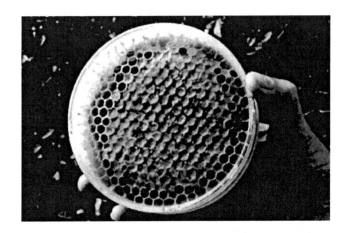

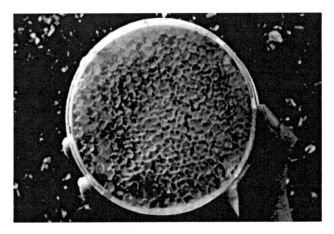

When a section is unfinished, the center can be cut out and the rest returned to the bees without foundation. These are three pictures of one and the same section.

temperatures around 57°F. It should, therefore, be stored in a heated house, and not in an unheated honey house.

Honey that is stored at a very low temperature, that is, at zero (F.) or below, in a freezer, will also be very slow to granulate, and can sometimes be stored that way indefinitely. I find it worthwhile to keep some of my comb honey crop over the winter this way in order to have it on hand earlier the following season. This does, however, tie up a freezer for a long time and, of course, incurs an additional cost of energy.

Probably the best single step you can take towards eliminating this problem is to get the comb honey crop sold quickly. Once in the hands of the consumer it is usually consumed quickly. It is, moreover, during the summer months that comb honey is most in demand, and this goes a long way towards eliminating the problem.

26. HOW TO MAKE SIMPLE COMB HONEY FRAMES.

Comb honey need not be conveyed to the consumer in small sections, whether these be wooden square sections or round ones. It can be sold in a regular unwired extracting frame, as noted.

Nothing so fancy as an extracting frame is necessary for this purpose, however. Something simpler, and in particular a frame without the top bar lugs, is preferable, and easy to make up.

Such a frame consists of no more than two end bars, of perfectly rectangular shape, and a top and bottom bar, somewhat narrower than the end bars but identical with each other. Nailed together, these four pieces make a rectangular frame, of the utmost simplicity, without protruding top bars.

More precisely, all four parts of the frame—top and bottom and both ends—should be cut from 3/8" stock. The end bars should be 1-3/8" by 4-5/8", and both top and bottom bars 1"x 17-5/8", which is the length of a standard bottom bar. Nail top and bottom bars to the end bars, and the frame is complete. It is not a sturdy frame, but since it will probably be used only once, and will not go into an extractor, this does not matter. It serves as a fine container for a section of comb honey weighing about four pounds, or the honey can be cut from it and marketed either as cut comb or chunk honey.

Such a frame must of course be fitted with foundation. A starter strip is sufficient, and in my opinion preferable to a full sheet, as it avoids the problem of the foundation warping and sometimes coming into contact with the foundation of an adjacent frame. It is also easier to fix into the frame. This can be done either by folding the edge of the strip and pressing it against the top bar with a spatula or putty knife, or making each top bar with a saw kerf or groove

76

and fixing the foundation therein with a bead of molten beeswax. Or indeed the top bar can be a split one, made up of two strips of wood, one of which can be nailed to the end bars only after the foundation is inserted.

Since such frames have no protruding end bars from which they can be supported in the super, then another means of holding them must be devised. This is exceedingly simple. Just nail a strip of sheet metal across each end of the super on the bottom, and let the frames rest on these

The advantage of making your own comb honey frames is that they are cheaper than purchased frames, and of a simpler, more suitable design. The only disadvantage is that the foundation must be affixed to the top bars, unless the top bars are of the split construction.

A simple homemade frame for producing bulk comb honey.

27. HOW TO PREPARE FRAMES FOR CUT COMB HONEY.

Certainly the easiest way to raise cut comb honey is to use standard size shallow extracting frames. Such frames should, how-

Split pins inserted through end bars keep foundation centered in the frame without using any wires.

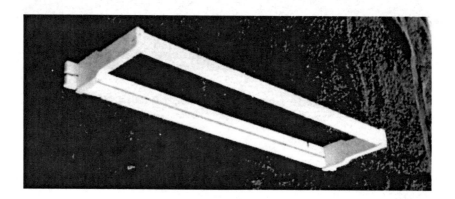

Bulk comb honey can be produced with unwired frames having split top bars.

A split top bar is spread to insert foundation by turning it 90° on two nail points spaced about 3/8 inch apart.

ever, have thin top bars and, for the utmost efficiency and simplicity, these should be split top bars. This enables you to insert foundation into the top bar, rather than having to fasten it by one means or another to the underside of the top bar. Frames with split top bars are sold by some of the bee supply companies for just this purpose.

If two small nails are driven through a pine board, such that they protrude about a quarter inch or so on the other side, and are spaced about 3/8" apart, then foundation can be fitted into split top bar frames very easily and rapidly as follows: Press the frame, upside down, over the nails, such that the nails enter the split from underneath. Turn the frame about a quarter turn, or 90°, which has the effect of spreading the top bar open. Now drop the foundation in, turn the frame back a quarter turn to its original position, and the two halves of the top bar will then come back together tightly enough to hold the foundation in place.

A starter strip of thin white comb honey foundation is all that is needed in such a frame—a strip perhaps two or two and a half inches wide is more than enough. The combs will be built straight in the frames of a super thus fitted with starter strips, provided ten frames are used and the hive itself does not lean off to one side, thereby confusing the gravitational orientation of the bees. Below the starter strip the comb is likely to be largely drone comb, but this makes little difference. About the only disadvantage of having honey stored in drone comb is that such comb is very attractive to the queen, who is likely to lay eggs along the bottom edges if no excluder is used.

Using full sheets, or nearly full sheets, of foundation in cut comb honey frames is no doubt desirable, provided some way can be found to prevent these sheets from bending and warping. Otherwise, the combs are very likely to be crooked and, worse yet, if the foundation in one frame should come in contact with the foundation in an adjoining frame, then the combs from these will be built stuck together, creating a real mess when they are removed.

Of course the foundation cannot be held straight in the frame by the usual method, namely, by wires. Bee supply companies do, however, sell split pins that are pushed into the holes of the end bars, holding the foundation in the center of the frame. If these are used they should be pulled out when the comb is built, preferably while the super is still on the hive, so that the bees can repair any slight damage or stickiness caused by pulling them out.

28. HOW TO FIT OUT A SUPER FOR CUT COMB HONEY.

It is not difficult to get bees working in supers fitted with extracting frames, which is an advantage of raising cut comb honey over section honey. Foundation by itself, however, is not attractive to bees, so they must be "baited" up into the supers, even for cut comb honey.

To do this, put two wired frames of drawn and (preferably) still sticky combs at the sides of the cut comb honey super, and between these, eight unwired frames of foundation, for storage of what will become cut comb honey. The bait combs will of course eventually be extracted. After the first such super, fitted with bait combs, the others can consist entirely of frames of foundation, though of course there is no harm in fitting additional supers with such bait combs too.

Whether such a super contains bait combs or not, it should always contain ten frames, and not less. If fewer frames are used the resulting combs are thick, bulging and often uneven.

A super of ten frames with split top bars for producing bulk comb honey. It is not necessary to use full sheets of foundation.

29. HOW TO DRAIN CUT COMB HONEY.

The edges of cut comb honey must be drained as dry as possible for either one of two reasons. First, if it is to be sold as cut comb honey, rather than as chunk honey, it makes a messy pack if it is not drained. And second, if it is to be packed with strained honey and marketed as chunk honey, then residual honey around the edges of the comb granulates quite quickly upon exposure to air and imparts granulation to the entire pack, rendering it unsaleable.

Some honeys do not granulate very quickly, and the foregoing rule can be modified for these. Most tree honeys, for example, such as basswood, are slow to granulate. Basswood comb honey packed as chunk honey need not, therefore, be drained dry before packing.

Pieces of cut comb honey must be drained in a warm room.

The manner of draining cut comb honey is simple. Make a rack using quarter-inch hardware cloth, and distribute the cut combs on this with a pan underneath to collect the drippings. The combs should be left thus in a warm room at least overnight.

30. HOW TO ASSEMBLE ROUND -SECTION SUPERS.

The plastic frames into which rings are inserted for round sections are designed to fit nine to a super, yielding thirty-six sections. It is, however, better to use only eight of them, leaving a space on each side of the super. A super that is thus ventilated on all four sides seems to be occupied more readily by bees (though some

Round sections freshly harvested, showing structure of the frame.
Section on the left will be returned to the bees to finish.

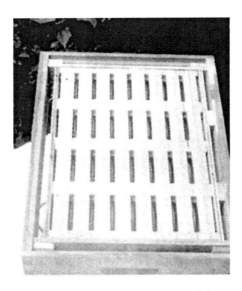

Round section super, assembled,
having ventilation on all four
sides.

experts deny this), and the sections at the sides are certainly finished up better.

To achieve this result, simply substitute for the ninth frame two strips of 3/8" plywood, the same size as the frame, on each side of the super. One of these should be cleated to hold it away from the side of the super and create the desired air space, and the other fixed the same way with two super springs.

Round-section supers are easily made up, either from scratch or by cutting down other supers, but the only way to get started with the equipment is to purchase a complete super, fitted with frames and rings. Thus you can see at a glance the precise design of the frames and how all the parts are fitted together. You can also get proper dimensions to guide your own carpentry.

A circular section super after many years of use. It is not necessary to clean or scrape the frames except to remove excessive burr comb on tops or bottoms, which is easily done with a hive tool.

31. HOW TO TAKE CARE OF ROUND SECTION EQUIPMENT.

Plastic frames should never be put in very hot water, otherwise they warp and become worthless. The only time they need to be cleaned at all is when they become sticky with honey, which is very seldom. In this case they can just be dipped in warm water or wiped with a damp cloth. It is seldom necessary to do more, by way of cleaning these frames, than pile the supers near the bee yard after the honey has been harvested from them. The bees not only clean out any uncapped sections left in them, but get every trace of stickiness too. Some of the uncapped sections can then be saved for use as bait sections (16), and the rest cleaned out and the wax thrown into a wax melter.

Plastic frames soon get considerable accumulations of burr comb on the tops and bottoms. This is easily scraped off with a hive tool when you are fitting the supers up with rings and foundation for reuse. If the burr comb is left there and becomes excessive it sometimes prevents supers below and above from resting close to each other, thereby leaving a crack between the supers. Bees are slow to put honey in sections that are near such openings to the outside, and worse, the spaces between supers can create a problem when it comes time to harvest them.

Rings that are left over can be used again, unlike wooden sections. They should be washed in warm water to remove the traces of honey in them, then given a rough scrape inside with a knife. Residual beeswax and traces of comb in them are harmless, provided they are not discolored.

32. HOW TO PREVENT EXCESSIVE BURR COMB ON CIRCULAR SECTION FRAMES.

Bees build burr comb on the tops of the frames when the space above them exceeds the bee space of 3/8 of an inch. It is important, therefore, to use supers of the correct depth, namely, 4 1/2 inches, no more. The depth of a regular comb honey super, that is, one used for square wooden sections, is deeper than this, and cannot be used with circular section equipment, no matter what other modifications are made in it.

One thing that renders it especially important to make this point is that one of the largest bee supply companies markets, as a circular section super, the deeper standard comb honey super. The result is not only a lot of burr comb on the tops of the frames, but burr comb that is filled with honey, creating a sticky mess when the honey is harvested and the frames are split apart to remove the sections. It is, indeed, an outrage that any manufacturer should offer equipment so manifestly unsuitable for its intended use.

The late Walter T. Kelley, famous Kentucky bee-keeper and promoter of cut comb honey.

Eugene Killion, Paris, Illinois, son of the great Illinois comb honey beekeeper Carl Killion, holder of innumerable awards and one of America's authorities on raising comb honey.

PART IV:
PRODUCING COMB HONEY
COMMERCIALLY

Pussy Willow

Packaging Comb Honey

THE SIMPLICITY AND REWARDS OF
COMMERCIAL COMB HONEY BEEKEEPING

Many years ago I got to corresponding with an old-time beekeeper who lived off by himself down in Pennsylvania. As I recall, he had some old bee books and journals I was interested in adding to my collection. Anyway, he eventually wrote that he was going to sell his farm and his bees and retire for good to the South.

Not long afterward, my travels took me near his place, so I went around to meet him, see whether he had any old books and journals I might want, and also any beekeeping equipment, since he said he was going to sell the whole works.

Well, we had a fine talk, and before leaving I bought some old bee journals he'd saved over the years. Then I thought I'd have a look at any bee equipment that might be up for sale. Beekeepers are notorious for having mountains of stuff around, and when you learn of one who's going out of business, it is usually a fine chance to pick up some bargains. But this gentleman had virtually no equipment at all, other than a few boxes of foundation and unused comb honey sections, still in their shipping cartons. He had a fine big apiary for sale at fifteen dollars a colony (this was in 1972), but that was it. And I had no way of transporting the bees. So that was a disappointment. Still, we'd had a good talk, and I had learned some things, as you always do when you talk with old-time beekeepers, and I'd gotten the old journals, so I was happy.

How come he didn't have the usual mountain of equipment—tanks, uncapping equipment, extractor, beeswax melting pots, and all that? Because he was strictly a comb honey beekeeper. And if you are a comb honey beekeeper you don't need much besides your smoker and veil and hive tool. And you don't need a honey house either.

Maybe that visit got me to thinking. In any case, a few years later I converted completely to comb honey beekeeping myself, and that was certainly one of the wisest decisions I ever made. I sold my entire extracting plant as well as several apiaries, keeping only the best ones, and began my career as a small commercial comb honey producer. I don't make my living at it, but it pays a considerable part of my livelihood, and it has convinced me that this is where the sideliner beekeeper should be. The advantages seem to be enormous, and besides this, it is more of a challenge. You can devote more of your thought and energy to improving your art and skill at beekeeping by this kind of specialization, rather than being just another run-of-the mill honey producer.

I had some moments of doubt before taking that step, but I never had any afterwards. It was a bit sad seeing my wonderful extracting plant dismantled and carted away, in spite of the large check I was holding in my hand. I had gradually perfected that extracting setup over the years, and it meant something to me. I could go out, all by myself, fill my thousand-pound honey tank, not with great ease, but with considerable efficiency, then bottle it up and spin out another thousand pounds. There was very little wasted motion and even the cappings ended up, at the end of one of my sessions at the extracting plant, as a bucket of pure wax, slowly hardening. Everything was done in a single orderly process and after the supers were in the honey house, I didn't have to lift a single drop of honey until it ended up in cans and jars at the other end. By that time it had gone through my flash warmer and was perfectly strained and there was nothing left to do with it but sell it. I really loved that setup, incorporated improvements in it from year to year, and I don't think anyone is ever going to design a better one for the beekeeper who does it all by himself.

But then I found that I was doing exactly the same thing every fall, namely, extracting tons of honey. It was no longer an adventure, no longer a challenge to my inventiveness and skill, and I was not getting any better as a beekeeper. It was just one big job. I don't object to work, but there is something seriously limiting in this kind of work, which is essentially repetitive. I had to spend quite a lot of time getting everything ready—uncapping machine cleaned, sharpened and ready to go, strainers attached, boiler heated up, steam hoses fastened here and there where they belonged, all that sort of thing. And then, once set up and going, I had to pretty much stay with it until at least forty, or more likely sixty supers were spun out. Otherwise, everything would cool down and it would take a while to get going again. And that was sometimes a drag. In fact my weekends during September and into October were largely devoted to the honey house and other things just had to wait. It was grand fun, and a good job, and a wonderful feeling to have all that honey to show for it. But as the years went by, it got to be less fun and more of the same thing I'd been doing over and over for years.

Well, the scene in my honey house, which for awhile seemed strangely empty, is different now. There are stacks and stacks of supers, beginning in July, but every single one of them is filled with round section comb honey, with the occasional exception of a super intended for cut comb honey. That elaborate extracting setup has been replaced by a simple pocket knife and a table. That's all I need, and the big table is useful for doing all sorts of work the year 'round. I go out there when I feel like it and pack up a half dozen supers or so, as I please, and that's it. If I want to stop and work in my garden or have some tea or talk with my wife, it is perfectly simple, and I can just go back to the comb honey later and pick up where I left off. And instead of spending so much

**The honey house equipment of the
comb honey beekeeper**

thought and energy on the harvesting of honey, I can spend it instead on tending my apiaries, which is where the real joys of beekeeping have always been for me.

It used to be supposed that comb honey beekeeping was a highly specialized aspect of the craft, and also laborious, involving a painstaking and time consuming assembly of sections and supers and then a laborious scraping of the wooden sections. Well, the perfection of round sections has changed all that. A super can be put together, ready for the bees, in fifteen minutes, and then when it has been finished by the bees, it can be taken apart and the honey all packed in twenty minutes without rushing at all. And there is no scraping of sections, because these round sections are designed in such a way that there is no way they can get propolized. The comb honey is worth about twice as much as strained honey, and the bees store it in the round sections about twice as fast as they do in the old square sections. So the purely practical advantages add up to a considerable plus. And besides this, there is the aesthetic consideration: Comb honey is the loveliest food that nature provides, and the only truly unprocessed sweet there is.

This is certainly the direction for part-time beekeepers to go. Leave extracted honey to the big commercial beekeepers, processors and packers. You can never compete with them in strained honey anyway, with their trucks, loaders, and their extracting and packing plants. They can process tons of honey in a day, more than you can do in a season, and buy their glass jars by the truckload at rock bottom prices. But by the same token, they cannot compete with you as a comb honey producer. They

91

don't have time to fool around with it. You do. And they can't pay that close attention to their bees to get the honey harvested while the cappings are still white and free from travel stain. You can. And they usually cannot be bothered selling honey a case or two at a time; they think in terms of drums of honey, sometimes in units of tons. But you can sell your comb honey a dozen or so sections at a time here and there, sometimes a few hundred at a time, and at the top wholesale prices— prices which, incidentally, will be at least four times, per pound, what the big commercial beekeeper will get for his strained honey.

So while the big commercial beekeeper will have certain advantages over you, you will have many, many advantages over him by raising comb honey, provided you are not trying to make your whole livelihood by beekeeping. You will get far more in relation to your investment in equipment and, if you genuinely love bees, more in terms of less tangible rewards. But the greatest single advantage of all, perhaps, will be the simplicity of your beekeeping and, to that extent, the simplification of your life.

Tom Ross, developer of Ross
Rounds equipment for
producing circular sections.

33. A SIMPLE APPROACH TO RAISING COMB HONEY COMMERCIALLY.

Some bee books give the impression that comb honey beekeeping is a highly specialized art, requiring complex management systems and lots of extra work. But that is not true in my experience, and I've been raising lots of comb honey for a long time. You can produce good crops of comb honey in about the same way you would extracted honey, by just putting comb honey supers on your hives instead of extracting supers. By adopting a few procedures that are not particularly time consuming, you can greatly increase your crop, but you need not, at any point, go into complex and laborious manipulations involving the dismantling of hives and so on. The basic procedure will remain the same, namely, supering over strong colonies that are, by relatively simple measures, prevented from swarming—which is the fundamental rule for producing honey, whether comb or extracted. Beyond this there are all the shook swarm systems and two-queen systems that can be used to produce truly spectacular crops, or to produce good crops in marginal areas where comb honey beekeeping might otherwise not be feasible. These systems, appropriate mostly for backyard beekeeping on a small scale, have already been described. But the point I am making now is that, if you keep bees in an area where there are fairly decent honey flows, then you do not *have* to go in for complex or specialized systems to get good crops of comb honey. You need only apply the basic principles of good beekeeping, supplemented by common sense and a thorough knowledge of bees.

That point really needs to be driven home, because almost every discussion of comb honey production in the literature of apiculture appears bent on making the opposite point. Readers thus get the idea that comb honey beekeeping is far too difficult and specialized for them, and they forthwith start sinking their money into extractors and all the other paraphernalia of honey production, imagining that they are thus following a simpler course! I have even seen a book which advocated, along with lots of complex and difficult manipulations, waiting until *after* the main honey flow has started before putting on any comb honey supers! And that is, for sure, an excellent recipe for getting a good crop of swarms, and mighty little comb honey.

What we have to remember is that the bees go about things in their own way, and make no distinction at all between comb honey and strained honey. What they do is build combs and, given the right conditions, fill them with honey. Those right conditions are, basically, strong non-swarming colonies and at least decent honey flows. No fancy systems and manipulations are going to change those conditions, or be a substitute for them. Given those right conditions, you will get a crop of honey, whether comb honey or extracted honey, and without them, you will not get much.

You don't have much control over honey flows. You take what nature gives you. Nor do you have any control over the weather. But you can, to a large extent, control the strength of your colonies, and thus make sure they are very strong, and that is over half the battle. With extracted honey, you can get away with supering a weak colony, and the worst that will happen will be a small crop from that colony. But half-filled comb honey sections are worth less than nothing. They are a bane and a headache.

Another principle to follow, involving no extra manipulation, is to get your entire comb honey crop from the summer flows, letting the bees have all the fall honey for their winter stores. There are several reasons for this, besides the obvious one of avoiding half-filled sections. You get your work finished up before the cold weather, for example. I always pity the occasional beekeeper I see out there taking off supers in November, and hauling them back to a cold honey house for tiresome days of extracting. You never need to do that if you are just into comb honey. Also, you want to get your comb honey crop sold, as much as possible, before winter sets in, so it should be harvested in plenty of time to do that. Summer is when people want to buy comb honey, and besides, you avoid the problem of granulation by getting it sold early.

Of course, nothing is perfect. I end up in the fall with a few comb honey supers still on the hives. These are usually supers into which I have gathered unfinished sections from the earlier harvests. The bees get most of them finished up so they are saleable. The few they don't finish I either use at home, or save to use for bait sections the following year.

Some beekeepers feel that they are losing good honey by not harvesting a fall crop. I used to think that way. But that isn't so. If you let the bees have all the fall crop—which means, goldenrod and aster honey where I live—then you will almost never have a winter loss. And equally important, the honey that stays on the hive and is not consumed as winter stores will be turned into bees the next spring, thereby satisfying the basic requirement of having strong colonies. *The heavier a colony is in the fall, the stronger it is going to be in the spring.* And it is all those extra bees in the spring that are going to be the foragers that give you your big crop of comb honey from the summer flows. Besides this, you will never have to feed your bees sugar syrup—which is just another needless and ex-pensive manipulation, adding to the work and overhead expense of beekeeping without any commensurate return.

The principle just enunciated—of ensuring strong colonies by hav-ing hives that are heavy with honey, not only in the fall, but still with

94

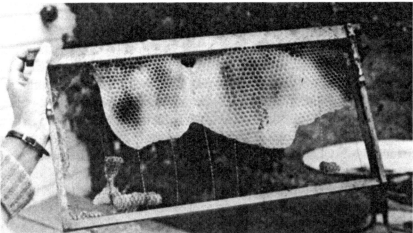

If a frame of foundation is given to the bees when there is no honey flow, they chew it up, especially where the wires are embedded. This can be overcome by feeding sugar syrup slowly. Foundation in bottom picture was replaced with drone comb.

plenty of honey left in the spring—is probably the most neglected principle of productive beekeeping. I have even known beekeepers who harvest every bit of honey they can in the fall, then feed sugar syrup to their bees for winter stores, imagining that they are going to come out ahead that way. It may look that way, when sugar is much cheaper than honey, but that is only half the picture. The other half is colonies of less than normal strength in the spring, and thus, a reduced honey crop that year.

The final secret of successful comb honey production is the use of round sections. The advantages of these, already noted, are so great and manifest that the old wooden square sections are certainly about to go the way of the straw skep, and deservedly so. Those square sections were fragile, laborious and time-consuming to assemble, and they almost never got filled up properly, that is, filled and capped to the edges. Worse than this, they became stained and propolized by the bees, and often quite unsightly even after being scraped—and the scraping of those wooden sections was surely one of the most tedious chores of beekeeping. They could be shelved only on their sides, otherwise they were almost certain to leak, whereas the round sections can be laid flat, and almost never become sticky. Round ones can even be mailed by ordinary parcel post, with reasonable packing, whereas the square sections could hardly be shipped by any means without considerable breakage. And best of all, from the beekeeper's standpoint, a super of round sections can be filled with honey and ready for harvest in less than half the time it takes the bees to fill a super of square sections, because the round sections hold less honey and have no corners to be filled. In spite of this, honey in round sections commands a price comparable to, and often equal to, honey in square ones.

Putting this last point somewhat differently, we can say that a round section of comb honey, which weighs a little over a half pound, sells for about double what a pound of strained honey in a jar will bring, whether figured at wholesale or retail. And this means that it nets the beekeeper almost four times as much. Thus, a quarter of a crop of comb honey in round sections is almost as valuable as a full crop of honey extracted. And it is a lot easier to produce, given all considerations, and certainly requires a great deal less equipment.

Generalizing on all that has just been said, the rule should be: Keep things *simple*. Make every motion and every step count, and don't pour money into things that are not needed. What you are trying to do is produce as much comb honey as you can with the minimum expenditure of work and overhead. Now, of course, it is fun sometimes to fool around with fancy systems and get from one colony as much honey as you would normally get from two. It gives you something to boast about and take pictures of. But if you are trying to produce comb honey commercially, even if on a fairly small scale, then you are apt to find that, with those special methods, you are likely to find yourself spending as much time on one colony as you normally would on several, so you don't really end up much ahead.

34. EXTENSIVE VS. INTENSIVE MANAGEMENT.

If you have only a few colonies of bees, perhaps fewer than a dozen, and plenty of time to work with them, then probably the best way to manage them is intensively, that is, by employing the shook swarm systems described earlier. Those systems, skillfully used, will

Strong colonies
produce big crops.

produce the largest crops *per colony*, and they will also enable a bee-keeper to get decent crops in marginal areas where comb honey beekeeping might otherwise not be feasible. They do require extra time and work, however, and are not practical for raising comb honey commercially.

To raise comb honey commercially, on the other hand, you need to have a fair number of colonies, more, in any case, than will enable you to spend a great deal of time on each. You need, in other words, to manage bees more extensively, less intensively. Twenty-five colonies will, in a reasonably good beekeeping territory, enable you to get about two thousand round sections in an average year, which would be about a minimal commercial production. A hundred colonies, in perhaps four apiaries, would, of course, yield about four times as many sections and this would be a crop of considerable cash value.

Needless to say, one would need to work up to a production of that magnitude fairly slowly, in order to find or develop the market for it—something that is easier in some parts of the country than in others. This is crucial because, unlike strained honey, comb honey cannot be just stored away in drums indefinitely until a sale is made. It must normally all be sold in the same season that it is produced to avoid problems of granulation. Comb honey that has granulated is still perfectly nutritious, but it does not sell well and should never be put on the market. An unwary purchaser, perhaps not realizing that he has bought honey that is granulated in the comb, is apt never to buy comb honey again. Storing comb honey in a freezer—not just in a cold room, which is the worst storage condition imaginable, but in a very cold freezer—will usually prevent granulation almost indefinitely. But this entails the expense of a large freezer, besides which, only a rather limited amount of comb honey can be thus kept, even in a fairly large one.

The way a commercial production of the minimum size here contemplated is achieved is by the use of many colonies, all efficiently managed, but not managed intensively. In other words, you try to get more honey by having more bees, not by doing more work. You get less honey per colony, but, with many more colonies, you get much more honey, and that is what you are after. The aim, therefore, is to have a system that gets the maximum result *with the least work*. And what this means is, essentially, strong colonies that occupy the comb honey supers quickly and do not swarm. Achieve that, with reasonably good flows, and you will have a lot of comb honey to sell. And you will have done it with no more work, and with a great deal less equipment, than would be needed to raise a comparable amount of strained honey.

35. HIVE SIZE.

I have about twenty-five colonies per apiary, and each is one and a half stories high. That is, each consists of a full depth hive body, or brood chamber, plus a shallow extracting super, the so-called food chamber, for the second story. This shallow super can be of any of the three different depths normally used for shallow extracting supers; that is, 5-3/4", or 4-3/4", or 6-5/8", it does not make much difference.

Normally, beekeepers in my area—upstate New York—where winters are often long and cold, have all their colonies two full stories high, that is, two full-depth hive bodies, and they super over these. And that is probably the correct size of hive for producing extracted honey. But it is larger than necessary, and indeed too large, for commercial comb honey production, because with so much room, the bees are likely to be slow in occupying the supers. The beekeeper who is raising extracted honey can super up over a two- or even three-story hive and the bees will go into the supers at once, especially if the combs in the supers are sticky. Comb honey supers, however, contain no honey and, except for a bait section, no drawn comb, and the bees are quite content to ignore them unless they need the extra room.

A one-and-a-half story hive, with the shallow story on the bottom, is the right size for comb honey. This colony was filling four supers by early July, and the top two are ready to harvest, with escape screen underneath them.

36. THE "LET ALONE"PRINCIPLE.

My basic one-and-a-half story hives are disturbed as little as possible. The bees are let alone, so that they can get on with their work of making comb honey. Supers are added and harvested at the appropriate times, but otherwise not much is done to the hives themselves. Rarely is it necessary to remove any combs. There are no periodic or routine inspections of the combs, even in spring, this being simply time wasted. When the swarming season commences, it is sometimes (not always) necessary to remove combs, but seldom at any other time. The only exception to this last statement is when I have reason to suspect something wrong—e.g., queenlessness—and that is very seldom.

Very early in the spring—as soon as dandelions and fruit bloom begin to appear, and well in advance of their peak bloom—a comb honey super goes onto each colony and two onto the strongest ones. Another super is added soon after, that is, within a week. There is no point in delaying this—the sooner the supers go on, the better. The bees should have time to begin occupying them before they are actually needed for honey storage. And you can sometimes be astonished at how suddenly, and how soon, they need them for honey storage. Better, therefore, to be a bit early than the least bit late.

37. HONEY AS A QUEEN AND POLLEN EXCLUDER.

No excluder is used, and none is needed. How come? Because that shallow second story still has quite a bit of honey in it *from the previous season*. And a queen bee will normally not cross up over combs with honey in them in order to lay eggs above the honey. So a super with honey in it is a fairly effective queen excluder. You are thus spared the need of this extra piece of equipment, which is fairly expensive and soon becomes fouled with burr comb, and you also eliminate a common obstacle to the motion of the bees in and out of the supers. It is not without reason that the queen excluder is sometimes contemptuously referred to as a "honey excluder." It is not always easy to get bees to occupy comb honey supers, so we are naturally reluctant to add any obstacle to their doing so. A super without bees in it is also a super without honey.

Not only that, but the shallow second story, with honey in it from the preceding year, also acts as an effective pollen barrier, especially if there is still considerable honey in the center frames. This is very important for comb honey production, especially if one uses round sections. The bees seem to have a predilection for storing pollen in these, and unless this is prevented, the loss can be considerable. Even a single plug of pollen in an otherwise perfect section can be a serious detraction, for it is likely to taste terrible when chewed into. Sometimes a pollen plug cannot be seen in comb honey until bitten into, making matters even worse. A queen excluder is, of course, useless for keeping pollen out of the supers.

A shallow super of honey does keep it out, however, even when that super is only partially filled. I have not found pollen in my comb honey for several years, and have raised many thousands of sections in that time. There was a time, long ago, when it was a very serious problem for me. That was when I thought I could super right over brood, without any intervening honey.

The explanation for the effectiveness of such a honey barrier is not hard to see, for one who understands the ways of bees. That is, the normal pattern of a brood nest is: Brood below, pollen above this, and honey above the pollen. Of course that is not absolutely invariant, but that is the usual pattern. You almost never find pollen stored *below* brood, and rarely is it stored *above* any significant amount of honey.

Thus, when there is a considerable amount of honey in the shallow second story of the hive, and especially when there is still honey in the center of that super, then not only will the queen confine her egg laying below that honey, the field bees will also confine their pollen storage below it.

38. THE TAYLOR PRINCIPLE.

The important points just made can now be expressed in this single principle, which I take the liberty of calling THE TAYLOR PRINCIPLE. Namely: The more honey you leave in the hive in the fall, the more honey will still be there in the spring; hence, the more bees there will be in the spring; hence, the faster the colony will build up to maximum strength, ahead of the flow, and the bigger your crop will be that year; and moreover, the less pollen you will find in the sections (approaching zero), and the less work and expense there will be for you in feeding struggling and therefore unproductive colonies.

Many an author of bee books has congratulated himself on discovering some grand new principle of apiculture or some great new system of management, but mine has this merit, at least, that instead of requiring *extra* labor and manipulation, it in fact *eliminates* much labor and manipulation, yielding bigger honey crops in the process. The principle simply requires that you *not* harvest honey that you *could* harvest. Essentially, you leave it in the hive *as an investment in your next year's crop.* It is an investment that pays a very good dividend indeed.

It is hard to imagine how a beekeeper could, at a single stroke and with such little effort, achieve so many different objectives—stronger colonies, bigger crops, the elimination of pollen or brood in the sections, hence the elimination of queen excluders, the virtual elimination of winter loss, and hence, the elimination of the need to feed bees.

It is also hard to imagine that this basic principle, which has some application to the production of extracted honey as well as comb honey, should be so widely disregarded, even by beekeepers of long experience. I have even known beekeepers to go into the *brood* chamber to remove a comb or two of honey and extract it, leaving the bees not only seriously weakened in stores, but inevitably weakened of bees later on when they are going to be needed. And the beekeeper who feeds his colonies sugar syrup in the fall has certainly failed to appreciate the points just made, and is, in fact, going backwards instead of forwards. The purpose of leaving plenty of honey on the hives in the fall is *not* just to save yourself the trouble and expense of feeding them to ensure their survival, either in the fall or the spring. It is also, and primarily, to ensure a large population of bees in the spring, and hence, a large crop of honey. It is of the very essence of productive beekeeping to have strong colonies. And the best, simplest and most direct way to achieve this is to have hives that are heavy enough in the fall to be still heavy in the spring.

Of course I am not the first to advocate leaving the bees with ample winter stores. But I am, in fact, advocating much more, namely, abundant spring stores as well, not just for survival and buildup, but for the several purposes I have indicated.

39. SWARM CONTROL.

Comb honey beekeeping, and the harvesting of bountiful crops, would be about the simplest thing in the world were it not for one other problem, and that is the problem of swarming. We now have before us a simple means of establishing the basic requirements of comb honey beekeeping, namely, the strongest possible colonies with the least work. But every beekeeper knows that, unless something further is done, this is also going to be the simplest means of getting the largest number of swarms, thereby defeating the ultimate objective of large crops.

An awful lot has been written about swarming, probably more than on any other aspect of beekeeping. You can find whole books on the subject. One British beekeeper, E. L. Snelgrove, made himself famous by his ingenious (and complex) methods of swarm control. It is something beginning beekeepers usually fret about a great deal. Sometimes they experiment with immensely complex manipulations, often ending up with hives several stories high, with brood chambers up on top, of all places, and a couple of queen excluders in the stack, that sort of thing. And that is certainly going in the wrong direction, violating the basic principle of simplicity.

There is really no point in bucking a colony that has decided to swarm. If you let them get to that point, then you have waited too long. Sometimes the bees will make preparations to swarm, building queen cells and everything, and then for no apparent reason just change their minds and tear down the queen cells. But you can't count on that. Other times you can knock yourself out trying to get them to stay put, and they'll merrily swarm in spite of it all.

So what you have to do is humor them. That is, you create with a few simple steps, at your own convenience, the basic result of swarming, so that the bees get it out of their system, but according to your schedule and plan rather than theirs. In other words, you split the colony, but in a manner that does not weaken it.

And here is how you do that.

You go up to a colony that is getting so strong you think it might start queen cells, or perhaps already has. But it is best to get to them *before* any queen cells get started; that is, queen cells with larvae and royal jelly in them. Empty little cell cups are of no significance. Now from that strong colony you take at least three, maybe as many as six, combs of brood and bees, trying to get mostly sealed brood. Get as little unsealed brood as possible. But also be sure there is some (not much) honey and pollen in at least one or two of the combs. Actually, if you take the combs right from the middle of the brood nest, you are likely to get combs more or less of this description. If, doing this, you pull out a comb having lots of unsealed brood in it, put it back and try another.

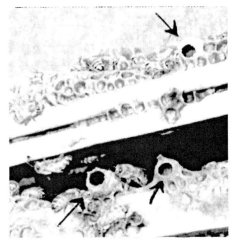

Little cell cups on the bottom of the frames of the upper story, resembling acorn caps but containing no royal jelly, are not an indication of swarming preparations and can be disregarded.

Don't get the queen. She has to stay there in the hive. Examine each comb as you take it out to be sure you are leaving the queen behind, but keep as many of the other bees on the combs as possible, by handling them gently. It is not necessary to *find* the queen; you need only ascertain her *absence* from the combs you remove. But of course if you do happen to see her, then you can take out whatever more combs you want without examining them for the queen, the comb with the queen on it being meanwhile set to one side, in the shade, and not near the hive entrance.

Put those combs into empty hive bodies, or into nuc boxes, at least three per hive or nuc, or as many more as you wish, but never fewer than three. You can put combs of brood and bees from different colonies into the same hive body or nuc if you want to, and they will not fight, because these are all young bees. The older flying bees, which would be the troublemakers, will have flown back to the hive, and the ones left on the combs you have removed will get along just fine.

Next replace those combs in the original hive with frames of foundation or drawn combs.

Result? Well, that strong colony now finds itself with three or more empty combs right in the middle of the brood nest, and the queen can't wait to fill them up with eggs. This, together with the considerable temporary reduction of population, tends to take the bees' minds off swarming. It goes against their nature to swarm when the whole center of their brood nest is completely empty of brood. If, in addition, you used foundation instead of drawn combs to replace the combs you removed, then the bees are exceedingly unlikely to swarm. They go to work building comb, instead, which keeps them busy for awhile, and uses up some of the wax they would need if they were going to fly off to a new home and build combs.

And have you weakened the colony by the removal of all those bees and brood? Not really, because in three weeks all the eggs that the queen lays in those empty combs turn into adult bees, and you have a very powerful colony indeed, with nothing better to do than make lots of comb honey.

The best time to do all that is when the bees appear to be on the brink, not of swarming, but of swarm *preparations*: or, in other words, just ahead of the swarming season. That would be early or mid-May in my area. And as for supering, your comb honey supers, at least two, should go on right away, as soon as you have made the split, not a week or two later.

If you now consider the procedure just described, you can see that it represents rather little work, hardly more than the removal of a few combs from a hive.

40. SWARM CONTROL FOR AN ENTIRE APIARY.

An entire apiary can be dealt with in the manner just described in only about an hour or so. My own procedure is as follows.

I arrive at one of my apiaries of about twenty-five colonies, and remove the covers, one at a time. I judge the strength of the colony by the concentration of bees on the inner cover. If there are rather few bees there, then I conclude that the colony is not yet up to swarming strength, and put the cover back on. That colony has now been dealt with so far as this visit is concerned, and it took only a few seconds. If, on the other hand, there are lots of bees on the inner cover—if the inner cover is virtually covered with bees, for example—then I know that this is a very strong colony, quite apt to swarm if nothing is done. So I leave the cover off that one, to identify it, as I proceed on through the apiary, checking under the rest of the covers.

Within fifteen or twenty minutes, I will have checked under every cover, and there will be perhaps a half dozen or so hives with their covers off, indicating that these are the ones most likely to swarm. In some years there will be more such colonies, even twice that many, and in other years only two or three, and, of course, a week or two later I may need to check again and deal with a few more. Seasons differ. In any case, I deal with all these strong colonies in the manner described above; that is, I split out at least three combs of brood and adhering bees from each. A few queens will be found in the process, but none will be searched for, nor are combs closely examined for queen cells, so rather little time is spent dealing with all the colonies needing attention.

That method of swarm control is not, of course, fool-proof. It does not reduce swarming to zero. But it does hold it down rather well, so that

The strength of a colony can be gauged by the number of bees on the inner cover. This strong colony will gather a good crop.

swarming is not a serious and crop-threatening problem and, of course, it does not demand much from the beekeeper in terms of time.

41. MAKING UP NUCS.

What, then, is to be done with the combs of brood and adhering bees that have been removed? You make up nucs with them, using either special nuc boxes or regular hive bodies (13). All my nuc boxes are three-frame ones, so there is nothing to do with these but give them new queens. I punch a nail hole in the candy ends of queen cages, and lay one of these, screen down, over the frames of each nuc. Acceptance of the queen is almost automatic, since the nucs contain only young bees, who rarely attack a queen when she is introduced in this fashion. Then I either leave the nucs there in the apiary, on top of regular hives, or cart them home with me. If left there, the entrances are stuffed loosely with a bit of grass, to prevent too many bees from escaping and wandering off. The older flying bees will have left already.

If, on the other hand, the combs of brood are put into hive bodies rather than nuc boxes, then the procedure is exactly the same, except that more than three, and as many as nine, can be put together into a single hive body. Then it is requeened in the manner described or, if advanced queen cells were found on the combs when they were trasferred to this hive, the new colony can just raise its own queen. I prefer,

105

Three-frame nuc boxes

however, to destroy any such queen cells that I find and introduce a new queen. The colony gets going more quickly that way, and is less likely to end up queenless.

This new hive can, instead of being set off onto a new stand and bottom board, be set right on another hive, or even on the hive the combs came from, with a double screen between it and the hive below, but with the entrance facing in the other direction. If you have no double screens, you can use a regular inner cover whose center hole has been screened over on both sides. The purpose of this double screen, with space between, is to keep the queens from making contact with each other. This procedure—putting the new colony right over an established one, with entrance behind—not only spares you the need, at least for the time being, of finding a new bottom board, inner cover and cover, but it also enables the new colony to benefit from the warmth that rises from the colony below.

If the colony thus created remains in the same apiary, then, as in the case of nucs, the entrance is stuffed with fresh grass, which in a day or two dries up and falls away. In case fewer than nine combs are put into such a hive, then, of course, additional combs are added at once to make up a total of nine. You must not leave a hive with fewer than this normal complement, even for a day or two, lest the bees start building a comb in the space left empty. And if foundation is used rather than drawn combs to fill up the extra space, then plan on feeding sugar syrup, starting in about a week or ten days. Do not begin feeding syrup before then, for this hive has no guard bees yet and it will be robbed dry and perish if offered a syrup feeder too soon.

The nucs or hives can be used to begin new apiaries or expand existing ones or, more likely, sold as is. I have always found a ready market for both nucs and hives among persons just beginning with bees, or beekeepers wanting to expand.

42. SUPERING.

Supers can be prepared in spare time during the winter months, provided you have a warm room to work in. If not, then you'll have to wait until spring because foundation gets brittle and breaks in a cool room. Nor have I been able to find a method for warming it without causing it to wilt or melt. In any case, by doing a few supers a day, as time and inclination permit, you can have an impressive accumulation ready when needed. Three or four supers of round sections can be made ready in an hour, so an hour or two each evening after supper, for a few weeks, will give you what you need. Spread out this way, the work is pleasant, as it goes along quietly and can be enlivened with recorded music or radio or, for that matter, with just your own peaceful thoughts.

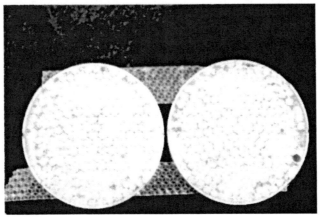

Given a decent flow, the bees will make perfect comb honey with only half sheets or even strips of foundation, but there is little saving in this.

It is standard practice to use full sheets of foundation, rather than to economize with less. In the case of round sections, this means one sheet of 3-7/8" foundation for each frame of four sections—which is, incidentally, the smallest of the standard foundation dimensions. In fact, however, a half sheet or less is perfectly satisfactory, so far as I have been able to tell, and sections offered to bees with foundation in only the upper halves get drawn out and filled indistinguishably from those fitted with full sheets. It is nevertheless my practice, and in keeping with the recommendations of all the best comb honey beekeepers, to use full sheets.

43. PESTS AND DISEASES.

American foul brood is an age-old problem for beekeepers and is dealt with in every book on practical beekeeping, so little needs to be said here. It plagues beekeepers more in some areas than in others. Indeed, some beekeepers, taking only minimal precautions, almost never see it, while others, located elsewhere, must be constantly on the alert. If it breaks out in a colony, then the only thing to do is kill the bees and burn the combs. You can usually prevent its occurrence, however, by giving the bees minute doses of Terramycin mixed with powdered sugar twice in the spring, at an interval of a week or so, before any supers go on the hives. It is a simple and easy procedure, taking but a few minutes, and it goes far towards solving the problem. A packet of Terramycin can be purchased cheaply at any store dealing in agricultural supplies. It will probably say on the label that it contains 10 grams of active ingredient (oxytetracycline hydrochloride) per 6.4 ounces, which means that it is TM-25, or that it contains 25 grams of Terra per pound. The entire pack can be thoroughly mixed with two pounds of powdered (not granulated) sugar, or smaller amounts can be prepared as directed on the label. The mixture has a long "shelf life" and can be stored in a dry place until the expiration date shown on the label.

The most troublesome pests, which have appeared quite recently on this continent, are parasitic mites. Tracheal mites, which have been known in the British Isles for years as acarine, are invisibly tiny mites that infest the trachea of adult bees. They are sometimes particularly troublesome when the bees are inactive, that is, in the fall, winter and early spring, as they then spread easily from bee to bee until, sometimes, the colony becomes so heavily infested that the bees simply abandon the hive. When the weather becomes warm and the bees become very active, tracheal mites usually cease to be a problem.

Varroa mites are a serious problem. These are large mites, easily visible, and they attack both the brood and the adult bees. This mite parasitizes the brood, especially drone brood, in the early part of its life cycle, and its presence can be determined by uncapping a few drone cells. If Varroa is discovered in a hive, then you can conclude that it is in every hive in the apiary, and the mites will, in time, destroy every colony unless measures are taken.

Fortunately, the Varroa problem is quite easily dealt with by the use of Apistan strips. These are inserted in the fall, after the honey harvest, according to the directions on the label, and they appear to be completely effective. Meanwhile, work is going forward on developing resistant strains of bees and it should be only a matter of time before this is achieved.

One other pest of recent origin, though a minor one, should be mentioned. This is chalk brood. It is a fungus which infects immature bees in their cells and these then appear, sometimes in considerable numbers, at the entrance, as white pellets—hence the name.

**Chalk brood is identified by small white pellets
at the hive entrance**

I have never known a colony to die off as a result of chalk brood, but it does sometimes cause considerable weakening of the colony, sometimes to the point that you get no crop at all from a hive thus infected. It seems to be self-limiting, however, as the bees continuously, by their housekeeping, clear the infected young from their cells and deposit them outside. I know of no effective way to combat it except, once again, by trying to maintain strong colonies.

The discovery of tracheal mites in America several years ago produced great alarm among beekeepers, bordering on hysteria in some quarters, and then the discovery of Varroa a few years later caused widespread gloom. These fears have since been mostly dispelled. I, for example, take no steps against tracheal mites other than to maintain strong and vigorous colonies the year 'round, and I take only the simplest routine steps against American foul brood and Varroa. And with the exception of only one year, I have, in the past several years gotten, year in and year out, record honey crops. It is often said that nothing succeeds like success and certainly success is proof enough that things are going all right. Pessimism is out of place here, and so are draconian measures. What is called for is simply good beekeeping practice.

44. MAKING SUPERS.

A beekeeper who wants to make his own round section supers, either from scrap lumber or from factory-made equipment such as hive bodies, should, in any case, *start* with a factory-made sample super. Manufacturers of round section equipment can supply such a sample super, assembled and fitted with frames, ready to be fitted with foundation and put on a colony of bees. With such a super on hand, you can see at a glance how it is assembled and you will have the correct dimensions for whatever additional supers you want to make up.

If you have a table saw, you can make all the supers you want from scrap lumber. The corners need not be dovetailed; a simple lap joint is sufficient. Comb honey supers are not, after all, subjected to much strain and are not in the apiary long enough to suffer damage from weather. The one important consideration is their depth. They are slightly more shallow than the standard comb honey super used for the old-fashioned square sections, being 4-1/2" deep. If your supers are deeper than this, you will get burr comb on the tops of the frames. This becomes damaged when the sections are removed, causing drizzling and general stickiness which sometimes drips onto the sections themselves. If, on the other hand, your supers are less than this depth, then you will have difficulty putting them on the hives without leaving a considerable crack where the supers come together. The 4-1/2" depth should, therefore, be quite scrupulously held to.

Existing equipment can be cut down to this size on a table saw. Alternatively, you can rip new, full-depth hive bodies, before they have been assembled, getting two supers from each such hive body. If you have no table saw, then someone who does can do the sawing for you, very quickly and easily if the hive bodies are new and unassembled. Since a round-section super is less than half the depth of a full-depth hive body, you will have strips left over after cutting them down. These can be nailed together and used to make very good double screens, which sometimes come in handy.

When two comb honey supers are made by ripping an unassembled full-depth hive body, then one of the supers will have hand holds and the other will not. But this problem can be overcome by ripping them in such a way that one of the supers will have hand holds on the sides only, and the other will have them on the ends only, so that each such super at least has two such hand holds. Actually, however, comb honey supers are so relatively light and easy to handle that it makes little difference whether they have hand holds or not.

Round section supers have an air space at each end and should, in my opinion, have them at the sides, too. This is accomplished by having a piece of thin (3/8") plywood fixed at one end and one side, held in place by thin cleats, (about 3/8"). Similar pieces of plywood are held in place on the remaining side and end with super springs. Hence, the frames will always fit properly, even when measurements are inexact, for the springs provide the needed flexibility.

A super will hold nine frames, but, in this case, there will be no air space at the sides, the entire internal width of the super being taken up by frames. What I prefer, therefore, is to use only eight frames in each super. I thus have a properly ventilated super, and the sections in the side frames, though drawn and filled last, are nevertheless finished up by the bees just as well as those in the center.

There is never any need to paint the inside of a super, and it is in fact best not to. Many beekeepers like to paint the outside white, but I prefer creosote. Properly used, this is probably the best thing to apply to all supers, hives and hive parts that are exposed to the weather. Stack the supers up, about ten to a pile, when freshly assembled and before they have been used, apply creosote with a big brush, and leave them there in the sun for a couple of weeks to dry. They soon dry completely to a rich, attractive brown, and the creosote is not, contrary to what is sometimes claimed, the least objectionable to the bees. And, needless to say, it does not, when dry, constitute the remotest threat of contamination to the honey that will eventually be stored inside, any more than ordinary paint would.

45. THE SOLAR WAX MELTER.

Even a comb honey beekeeper accumulates a considerable amount of beeswax in the course of the season, largely from scraping the burr comb from the plastic frames. Since this wax is not admixed with the resins and fiber found in old brood combs, it can be melted down very nicely, and at no cost, in a solar melter.

My melter consists of nothing but an old bee hive painted black with a scrap of plywood nailed to the bottom, a slightly sloping trough to hold the wax scraps, and a glass laid over the top. Tilted so as to catch the sunlight as directly as possible at the height of the day, the device melts down a large amount of wax each sunny day, the wax drizzling into a cottage cheese carton or whatever is handy. I remove the block of wax each morning, refill the trough with wax scraps and replace the carton.

111

A simple solar wax melter.

There is no need to pay a cent to get valuable, high-quality wax from what would otherwise go to waste. It can all be traded for the foundation the comb honey beekeeper always needs when the new season begins.

46. COLONY IDIOSYNCRASIES.

Colonies differ with respect to how they make comb honey. Some, for example, leave a slight space beneath the cappings, so that the sections, unless travel stained, are sometimes almost snow white, while other colonies plaster the cappings down against the surface of the honey, resulting in a much less attractive product, even though the honey in each type of section may be identical. Again, some colonies leave a hole in the bottom of the section as a passageway. These are sometimes referred to as "communication holes", and one occasionally finds them in every section of an otherwise perfectly finished super. These in no way affect the quality of the honey itself, but they detract from the appearance of the section, giving the impression of its being unfinished even though it may, in fact, be full weight.

A more serious problem is the tendency of some colonies to attach a bridge of brace comb to the surface of the sections. The result is that some of the cappings, often in the very center of the section, get pulled away when the honey is removed from the super, creating a drizzle. The beekeeper sometimes finds that the bees have done this to most of the sections in the super, so it can be a real problem, considerably reducing their saleability. Sometimes, but not always, these bridges of burr comb can be severed with a sharp knife before removing the sections, thereby preventing damage to the cappings.

You will sometimes find plugs of pollen in comb honey sections, making them unsaleable, for these pollen plugs, when visible, are unsightly, and invariably taste bad. Anyone encountering one of them and not knowing what it is would be unlikely ever to use comb honey again. These pollen plugs are not the result of colony idiosyncracy, however, but of poor management on the part of the beekeeper. They come from having a super too close to the brood nest, especially with a colony that has just recently been established in a single story hive, or when comb honey is produced by the "shook swarm" method (8).

The worst colony idiosyncracy I ever saw— and I saw it only once in my many years of getting comb honey—was the cross-wise construction of comb in my supers. The bees simply ignored the foundation and built their combs at right angles to it, filling the super with honey that it was impossible to harvest. That this was no accident of mismanagement, or the result of perhaps neglecting to insert the foundation in that super, was shown by the fact that this colony had done exactly the same thing with the next super I took from it!

Something like that is, of course, very rare, but it drives home the fact that the behavior of bees can differ quite radically from one colony to another.

Colony differences such as those just described point up the desirability of having the right kind of queens to head the colonies of comb honey hives; that is, queens whose progeny make white cappings rather than plastering them to the honey underneath, and which do not build brace comb or create communication holes. No doubt the most reliable way to achieve this would be to raise your own queens from colonies having the desired traits. If you do not have time to do this, then it is at least worthwhile to keep some track of which colonies make the nicest comb honey, and noting where those queens came from.

47. SELLING COMB HONEY.

A comb honey beekeeper has some special marketing problems and, if you go into raising comb honey commercially, you will have to meet and solve these problems as you expand. A thousand sections are not hard to sell, for anyone who is the least resourceful, but before you suddenly find yourself with two or three times that number, you had better have lined up at least a potential market for them.

There is no doubt that the best way to sell comb honey is at a roadside stand, especially if it is where tourists pass by. Tourists, who are by their very nature lovers of things novel and different, are great buyers of comb honey, many of them having never seen it before. And many people who are not tourists nevertheless love roadside stands, and with good reason. It is there that they can get fresh produce, often from the very person who raised it. Wherever your honey is offered for sale, make sure it will be seen. The minimum requirement is that it be at eye level. Better yet is to have it stacked near the cash register where it will come under the eye of every single customer.

You need several big signs up and down the road for a successful honey stand.

People rarely put comb honey on their grocery lists. It is what is known as an "impulse" item, something people will buy only if it catches their eye. This is the crucial consideration for the comb honey beekeeper.

It is, incidentally, in the light of this consideration that round sections can be seen to have another considerable advantage over the traditional square ones, for they do have great eye appeal. They are usually, or at least should be, filled pretty much to the edges, and the capped surface is clearly visible over its entire area. Piled one atop another, perhaps six or eight deep, it becomes almost irresistable to anyone to pick up the top one for a closer look and then, fairly regularly, to purchase it.

When I have left comb honey at grocery stores and supermarkets, and left it to the management to shelve it, the result has almost always been disappointing. It simply goes unnoticed. At roadside stands, on the other hand, even people who have never heard of comb honey are likely to buy it, then come back for more.

If you are not situated on a highway where you can set up your own stand, or if you are too busy for this, distribute your product to others. But if you set up your own stand, place it within clear view of your house to reduce the temptation to theft, and let people serve themselves by the honor system. The other essential is that you post large signs on the highway, in both directions, and preferably up to a mile away, proclaiming that honey is for sale. It is of no use to you for travelers to get the impulse to buy just as they are passing your stand.

Beyond this, you should be on the lookout for persons to sell to at wholesale, either in small or large lots. Proprietors of roadside stands and fresh food markets should have their sales guaranteed. This is accomplished by your offering to repurchase any honey that is not sold by a certain time. You will seldom need to buy any back and meanwhile, your customer is freed from risk.

Other persons will buy sections from you two or three hundred at a time, and often more. These are the buyers for natural foods stores and other specialty shops. You find these people by asking around. I have come to know several of them over the years and I keep a list of them, with telephone numbers and addresses, in my shop. I have had such buyers drive hundreds of miles to load up with comb honey, sometimes taking every last section I had, but normally I am expected to deliver to them. I do this, of course, only by combining such deliveries with other trips. Thus, if I know I am going to be in Connecticut, say, at some future date, I arrange in advance with buyers there to deliver whatever honey they may want. All it takes is a bit of resourcefulness and, of course, a good product which mostly means, in the case of comb honey, sections that are well filled and capped over. It does not require any special talents of salesmanship.

My "self serve" honey stand

48. THE HOME HONEY STAND.

The advantage of selling honey at your house, from your own honey stand, is that you get a retail price. It takes a bit more time because customers sometimes want to stop and talk, but there are, nevertheless, other rewards.

My own honey stand has not only been profitable for me over the years, it has also been a pleasant pastime. I'm on a good highway and people can drive right into the yard and up to the stand to have a look. Large 4' x 8' signs, a mile up and down the road, announce COMB HONEY and smaller signs repeat the message closer to home so that when a car finally arrives at the house, its driver and passengers know what to expect.

Oh, it is fun doing it that way. I wander out and talk with the people if I happen to see them and if they look interesting, though, in fact, most of my customers come and leave unseen. I find the supply of honey reduced, but the supply of cash in the "honor box", as it is labeled, is properly augmented. The two usually tally out just right. Very few people are thieves. Sometimes, when they encounter me there, they are impressed to see a real live beekeeper and that, of course, gives me the pleasant feeling of being a little more important than I really am. Often they are young people going here and there camping, sometimes on bicycles, and I always talk with them when I see them to see what they're thinking about. That's the best way I know for trying to keep myself from becoming a tedious old fool. Sometimes customers note the large pooh-bear mounted atop the stand and laugh with joy. It gives the establishment a nice touch. And sometimes just the sight of an institution, however modest, that is based on the trust of one's fellow men, seems to redeem people's faith in things. Actually my trust is not absolute. I'm always somewhere around when the honey stand is open, and I have a fair idea of what's going on there. A little sign in the top of my stand, which not everyone sees, says EAT HONEY, LIVE FOREVER. Some who read that are skeptical, but I offer myself as living proof. When I proclaimed myself the originator of that epigram, one customer thought I was alluding to another sign to be found there which reads THOU SHALT NOT STEAL. I confessed that I was not the author of that one.

I suppose that if any expert from the school of business and management were to do an analysis of my marketing, add up all the time I spend talking with people, trotting back and forth to the house to make change, repairing honey signs that have blown down, and all this, then he would declare that I have a very inefficient operation. Maybe so, but he would be on the wrong track because he would have no way of punching the joy factor into his calculator. And that factor is, after all, the only one that counts in the long run.

49. OVERWINTERING.

Overwintering colonies is less of a problem for the comb honey beekeeper than for one who produces strained honey. The main factor in successful wintering is an abundance of stores and this requirement is much more likely to be met in colonies that are managed for comb honey. Producers of strained honey are likely to harvest all the supers quite regardless of the amount of honey in the hive below and then, finding their colonies light on stores, resort to feeding sugar syrup in a desperate effort to compensate. Colonies managed for comb honey, on the other hand, almost invariably have plenty of honey in the hive below the supers, even when smaller hives are used.

The first step in wintering, therefore, is to check each hive for weight. This does not at all require actually weighing them. You simply lift each hive from behind, an inch or so, and form an instant judgement. It will probably feel as though it is filled with rocks and that is exactly as it should be. I never feed my colonies in the fall, nor, for that matter, in the spring either, with the rare exception of a colony that has come through the winter weakened. As has been noted, (38), the more honey there is in the hive in the fall, the more there will be in the spring and the more honey there is in the hive in the spring, the more bees there will be and the more brood there will be, and you will then already have met the main requirement of good management, which is, *strong colonies*. This point can hardly be overemphasized. It is at the very heart of good beekeeping. Waiting until spring and then trying to build up your colonies with sugar syrup will not achieve the same result. Indeed, I consider the routine feeding of sugar syrup to be a mark of incompetence in the art of beekeeping. When I hear a beekeeper speak of "emergency" spring feeding, that is, feeding to forestall starvation, then I feel that this beekeeper has already essentially failed. We want colonies in the spring that are not merely alive, but strong, especially if we are trying to get comb honey.

Hives tipped forward, ready for winter

The other requirements for wintering are good ventilation, unobstructed entrances, and protection from mice. These are met as follows.

1. Ventilation. The purpose of winter ventilation is not to provide fresh air to the bees, but to prevent the buildup of moisture. Bees do not hibernate, but remain active throughout the winter, maintaining warmth within the hive and, in doing so, they give off much moisture. This sometimes even freezes, as frost on the inside of the cover, and then,

when it eventually melts and drips down on the bees, it puts them under a severe stress.

Winter ventilation is achieved by having some sort of small opening near the top of the hive. One way to do this is to leave the inner cover hole partly open, provided the hive cover does not fit too tight. Or, a small crack can be made under the inner cover using a small pebble or nail as a wedge.

A scrap of tar paper over the entrance keeps out winter wind without obstructing ventilation

2. The unobstructed entrance. Sometimes the hive entrance can become obstructed by dead bees. If the colony is under some kind of stress, the accumulation of dead bees can become considerable, putting the colony under even more stress and threatening to clog the entrance completely. The beekeeper is then likely to find his hive a foul smelling and sodden mass.

The avoidance of this is very simple. Do not use a wooden entrance cleat that reduces the entrance to a small slot. Instead, leave the entrance wide open and clear, with the protections described below and, most important, tip the hive forward slightly by putting a stick of wood under it in back. This slight slope of the bottom board is usually sufficient to ensure a clear entrance and the absence of dead bees in the bottom of the hive.

3. Protection from mice and wind. Mice love to hollow out a cavity in a hive and fill it with filth, ruining many combs. When the bees are

clustered above, they offer little resistance to this. The way to keep mice out is, first, to have the hives up off the ground, preferably a foot or more, and second, to fix a wedge of hardware screen in the entrance. This should be held there with a couple of staples or thumb tacks, for otherwise it may be pulled loose by a skunk. Then, having done this, slap a scrap of roofing paper or tar paper over the entrance, fixing it there with a couple of staples. This fits fairly loosely so that the bees can still get in and out around the edges and it prevents a cold wind from blowing directly into the hive.

A wedge of hardware screen keeps mice out

Bees do not suffer by being buried in snow

It will be noted that nothing has been said about wrapping the hives. Wrapping, in my opinion, does more harm than good. On a sunny winter day, the inside of the hive can become abnormally warm, causing the bees to fly out and die by the hundreds in the snow. What bees need is not protection from cold, but from the stress factors described above. They can even become buried in snow without apparent harm.

120

50. HOW TO ACHIEVE TOTAL SUCCESS.

Henry David Thoreau declared that the only truly successful person is one who is doing exactly what he wants to be doing. Dr. C. C. Miller, who was probably the greatest comb honey beekeeper who ever lived, made precisely the same declaration and, putting that view of things to practice, he abandoned the medical career for which he had been trained in order to keep bees the rest of his life. Eventually his books and articles on beekeeping became an inspiration to the generations of beekeepers who followed him, for they were filled not only with his practical knowledge of apiculture, but with his own deep and simple human goodness and his love for God and all of creation.

Beekeepers have varying standards of success. Some believe that it is measured by the number of colonies one accumulates. This has always seemed to me absurd, even an intrusion of certain values into beekeeping which have no place there at all. I have found, moreover, that the ablest, best and most knowledgeable beekeepers are not those whose holdings are very great. These latter are often very knowledgeable indeed about the marketplace, but less often, reliable sources of information about the finer points of beekeeping.

This is not, of course, to suggest that considerations of income are out of place in apiculture. They need not be at all. One of my own great satisfactions is in getting good crops and in making quite a lot of money selling them, whether I can really claim to need that money or not. I see no reason why one should not think in such terms. Indeed, if someone aims to make his livelihood or even a considerable part of it at beekeeping, then common sense dictates a proper regard for profit and loss, and businesslike methods. The real danger, however, is in measuring success by that standard alone so that beekeeping, as an art or craft, becomes subordinate to increasing one's hoard of gold, the bees simply being a means to that end. To live a full, rich life, in which one has perhaps more than the common share of the golden hours, is one thing and something not easily achieved. To live a life whose riches are chiefly in gold itself, with little regard to any other treasure, and particularly the treasures of the spirit, is another thing. And while the latter is no doubt the most common measure of success, it most assuredly diverts one from the path of that true success that Thoreau and Dr. Miller were thinking of.

INDEX

Lightning Source UK Ltd.
Milton Keynes UK
UKOW021007091012

200259UK00003B/6/P

9 781908 904188